PENGUIN BOOKS

SĪTĀ'S KITCHEN

Ramchandra Gandhi has contributed several articles on the Ayodhya question to national newspapers. He is the author of four other books. He has been Professor of Philosophy at the University of Hyderabad, Professor of Comparative Religion at Visva-Bharati, Professor of South Asian and Comparative Philosophy at the California Institute of Integral Studies, and a Senior Fellow of the Indian Council of Philosophical Research. He is currently engaged in research on the sages of modern India, and is a consultant on culture to the Indian National Trust for Art and Cultural Heritage.

SĪTĀ'S KITCHEN

A Testimony of Faith and Inquiry

RAMCHANDRA GANDHI

PENGUIN BOOKS
[redacted]

Penguin Books India (P) Ltd., B4/246 Safdarjung Enclave, New Delhi—110029, India
Penguin Books Ltd., 27 Wrights Lane, London W8 5TZ, UK
Penguin Books USA Inc., 375 Hudson Street, New York, N. Y. 10014, USA.
Penguin Books Australia Ltd,. Ringwood, Victoria, Australia.
Penguin Books Canada Ltd., 10 Alcorn Avenue, Suite 300, Toronto, Ontario M4V 3B2, Canada
Penguin Books (NZ) Ltd., 182-190 Wairau Road, Auckland 10, New Zealand
First published by State University of New York Press, Albany 1992

Published in Penguin Books 1992

[redacted]

For my former students and colleagues
at the California Institute of Integral Studies

CONTENTS

PREFACE

This book, a dialogical narrative with a prologue of contextualizing meditations, is a testimony of faith and inquiry: faith in the urgent relevance of India's spiritual traditions to the future of life and civilization on earth, and inquiry into the meaning of such central notions of these traditions as ātman or self, śūnyatā or emptiness, ahiṃsā or non-violence.

The narrative is a philosophical and fictional exploration of the meaning of a Buddhist story which records the Buddha's advice to a group of aristocratic revelers in a forest to abandon their hunt for an alleged prostitute who has decamped with their valuables, and to seek instead their self. A forest colloquium is convened by the nihilist masters Ajita Keśakambalin and Makkhali Gośāla, known contemporaries of the Buddha and Mahāvīra, to debate the issues arising out of the Buddha's ideologically subversive advice to spiritually starved aristocracy. Testimonies of faith and inquiry are offered under nihilist interrogation by a number of participants, including the Buddha. What is at stake is the honor of spiritual traditions; the worthwhileness of life itself is in question.

The Prologue recounts a recent visit of the author to Ayodhyā, believed by Hindus to be the capital city of God-incarnate Rāma's Kingdom on Earth, where the honor of India's spiritual traditions is being severely tested by a controversy surrounding a sixteenth century mosque alleged to have been built at the site and over the precise spot marking the birthhplace of Rāma. The author discovered that the same site is also revered as the Kitchen of Rāma's wife Sītā, who is esoterically the Divine Mother herself, compassionate nourisher of all creatures of the earth. The author suggests that Sītā's Kitchen must have been a sacred aboriginal grove in antiquity dedicated to primordial generativity; and that a deeper understanding of the site's significance can not only resolve the Ayodhyā dispute but also help dissolve the pervasive dualism of "self" and "other" which is hurling civilization headlong toward annihilation. The kitchen shrine is a real presence in the book's narrative too, drawing its events towards enlightenment.

ACKNOWLEDGMENTS

Whatever be the fate of life and civilization on earth, my own fate during the last eight years as an independent scholar would have been precarious without financial support, for which thanks are due to the following institutions:

Centre for the study of developing societies, New Delhi, for a grant under their United Nations University program; *Indian Council of Philosophical Research*, for a Senior Fellowship; *Central Institute of Indian Languages*, Mysore, for a grant; *Indian National Trust for Art and Cultural Heritage*, for a consultancy grant.

I am grateful to Mr H. K. Kaul, Librarian of the India International Centre library, and his staff, for working facilities and services without which I would not have been able to meet publication deadlines for this book; to Mr B. L. Mishra for typing the manuscript of the book; and to Professor Probal Dasgupta and Ms B. Shyamasundari for previewing and proof-reading the manuscript at short notice, and for the encouragement of their response to it.

Finally I would like to thank Mr William D. Eastman, Director of SUNY Press, for his interest in my work and for undertaking to publish this book; and Ms Christine M. Lynch, SUNY Production Editor, for her helpful suggestions and patience with proofs.

Ramchandra Gandhi
March 2, 1992
Mahāśivarātri

PROLOGUE

1

I virtually grew up in a newspaper office where my father worked as editor, and which was as much home to me and my siblings as the flat above the office where we lived.

I am a middle aged man now, but a quite recent dream of mine situated itself in what looked and felt and smelt like one of the big rotary machine halls of the old Hindustan Times building in Connaught Place in New Delhi; childhood's cocooning nursery.

Alone, I found myself deposited in a corner of this enclosure dominated by giant printing machines; born to them, as it were, with a sense of being covered with the placenta of machine grease. It felt like war time, newswise. This does not surprise me, because the years 1939–1945 and their newspaper after-life were years of impressionable childhood which presented themselves to me—or seem in recollection to have done so—as a collage of newspaper pictures of soldiers and tanks and airplanes, Hitler and Churchill and Subhash Chandra Bose; quite overshadowing, as far as I was concerned, the final phase of India's struggle for independence, a confession embarrassing to the adult Indian patriot in me but true to memory.

The room of the dream had one long open window which seemed inexplicably narrow, but the sky outside it was clearly visible, and so were a cluster of military airplanes which soon filled a high and distant portion of it. And those planes dropped bombs which looked in my dream, as they do in movies, like great Brancusi birds descending successively, legs folded. But unlike in the movies, the bombs then flocked together and proceeded to move horizontally, and frighteningly, towards the open window of my sanctuary. Entering the room through the window with quiet absurdity, they hit nothing, and dissolved into nothingness.

A second set of airplanes appeared in the sky and dropped bombs which, as before, straightened up after falling a certain distance and moved laterally towards the window. I noticed what

I hadn't the first time round, namely, that the bombs were wrapped in newspapers. Sailing through the window as before with implausible ease, they moved towards me but dissolved harmlessly again into invisibility without making any impact; it seemed as though they had been attracted and absorbed by the big machines into their inky substance.

The planes came around a third time and dropped their brood of newspaper-wrapped bombs which journeyed as before towards and through the window, towards me. Somehow I knew that this time it was going to be a hit and not a miss. Hit it was, the singular moment immediately preceding it liberated from anxiety by the certitude of catastrophe. I waited for an explosion, a shattering of things, the ending of life, pain and annihilation. But everything now dissolved into light not darkness. I felt merged in a blissful silence, emptiness, full of reality, without pain and without a sense of anything having come to an end; except fear. I thought, I felt certain, that I had died; but I also saw this was peace not agony or loss.

Then from the depth of that peace and light and silence rose three words in a feminine voice: "I love you." Words of frequent hypocrisy and deluding inaccuracy in waking life; but they rang deep and true in my dream. I woke up and have pondered the meaning of this dream for a long time now. I find revealed in it both contemporary and timeless truth, personal and universal meaning, at various levels of symbolism and suggestiveness, clarity and obscurity.

I am not unaware that the dream is littered with items of psychoanalytic significance, that much biographical embarrassment and enlightenment can be painfully and even liberatingly excavated from its suggestive imagery of closure and intrusion, submission and approbation, imprinting and identity; and so on. But I do not seek the liberation of adulthood from childhood and will not here follow the dream's lead in this direction.

I find vastly more exciting the themes of moral responsibility and spiritual literacy, causality and communication, anxiety and advaita, which the dream introduces and illumines; and not only for philosophical but also for personal reasons. For these themes remind me of my indebtedness to parents, teachers, and to Gods, the latter perfectly represented by Śrī Ramana Maharṣi, advaita's unique avatāra in our age, whom I never met in the flesh; but without whose grace I could not have comprehended the non-dualist significance of the Buddhist story which this book seeks to unravel as an integral vision of Indian spirituality of urgent relevance to the fate of life on earth.

The following readings of my "newspaper-wrapped bombs" dream are thus a dedication of this book of bhakti and vicāra, devotion and inquiry, to ancestors, preceptors, and Gods, in discharge of our limitless debt[1] to whom alone can life be self-realizingly lived: and an introduction to the idea and reality of "Sītā's Kitchen," as it turns out.

2

Although my father was himself an assiduous practitioner and custodian of fair journalism, he would have had no hesitation in admitting that untruthfulness and partisanship in journalism have greatly harmed the cause of freedom and justice and peace in our times: that bombs of hate have often been propelled by the machinery of newspapers, "wrapped" by them in respectability. Indeed all modes of public discourse and communication have sheltered falsehood and prejudice in our age.

Severely damaged credibility is the kārmic consequence invited by all orders of speaking for this sin against truth and impartiality. The encoding of this warning in the dream's retributive rhythm bears the strong imprint of my father's, and his father's, moral sternness; even as its reassuring consummation embodies their faith that contrite confession of guilt can only liberate the soul from the thraldom of ignorance and not harm or destroy it. May peace be upon their souls.

3

The stroke which eventually killed my mother had deprived her of the motor ability to write. I remember the day when a bank official came with an important document for her to sign. Tears rolled out of my mother's eyes as she let her thumb impression be taken in place of a signature. She suffered not only because, though a writer, she could not write. Her disability broke her heart, I am convinced, because it prevented her from inscribing Goddess Lakṣmī's name when occasion demanded this, for Lakṣmī was her name too. Close to death, she — a Brāhmaṇa woman of wide social sympathy who belonged to an ancient South Indian tradition of Vaiṣṇava bhakti — would not have wanted to appear to be denying, even under duress, that all creation bore the imprint of Lakṣmī; who, as Mahālakṣmī, is no mere consort of Viṣṇu, but herself ultimate reality, Godhead, Divine Creatrix.

Nothing is unreadable in the light of Mahālaksmī, who is also Sītā. Even violence is not an illegible, unredeemable, irrationality at the heart of the nature of things; it too bears witness to Sītā's maternal indulgence of creaturely folly and notoriously longs in embarrassment to destroy itself, a very long time though it often takes to do so.

It was my mother who taught me to read and write, and who tried less successfully to teach me to be patient and discriminating in the practice of living. I take the newspaper-wrapping of the bombs of my dream to be her characteristic reassurance that properly understood, read, unmasked, hostility can be defused without hostility: a lesson in practical, but not fundamentalist, nonviolence, for which I offer thanks to her spirit.

At a deeper level, this lesson is an intimation of non-duality: of the truth that apparent others are not other than self, only another image of self. During the last few hours of my mother's life, as she slipped steadily into the coma of death, I had ceaselessly chanted the names of Śrī Rāma and Śrī Ramaṇa. No doubt by their grace, Amma attained the form and formlessness of Mahālakṣmī, self and source of all.

4

Apparent otherness is undoubtedly a disguise of self, but what a powerful disguise it is! Let us make no mistake about this, let us not sentimentally deny the terrifying face of world-appearance.

The patch of sky visible from the window of my dream citadel can be seen as representing *nothingness,* that which devours all generations of all life, that into which all existence eventually vanishes: an undefeatable adversary. Equally adversarially, the airplanes which manifest in the sky and the bombs they drop can be seen as imaging invincible inorganicity: the causal furies and missiles of materiality in the midst of which life coweringly survives, and only briefly.

No less disturbingly, the missiles can represent the pervasiveness and penetrativeness of microbiological malevolence against which nothing that lives is immune, a symbolism which more generally draws attention to the unavoidable violence against life which sustains the life process itself. There can be no doubt that this embarrassing fact of life offers at a subconscious level a rationalizing encouragement to the wholly avoidable violence we practice against one another and against nature; and at a deeper level still it probably erodes the will to live and help live.

The bombs as bombs in their cycle of return in the dream can be seen by the despairing imagination as representing the apparently unmitigatably destructive and self-destructive power of dualism in human life: but not as a newspaper delivery-system. The dream comically invites an alternative saving non-dualist reading of intolerable appearance.

5

The slice of sky visible through the window of the machine room can be seen as representing the self-restraint of circumambient emptiness which does not overwhelm all existence, miraculously improbably; and which can be "read" as a newspaper whose blankness allows itself to be covered with meaningful marks which image emptiness' own meaning as a not-thingness, i.e. as self, indubitable reality which is not a thing among other things and in competition with them; but which all things image, well or badly.

In its intelligibility and in the interconnectedness of its particularities, materiality is a magnificent image of the luminosity and autonomy of self. As is non-human life in its massive demonstration of vitality and ecological restraint a pointed representation of the unfetteredness and sufficiency of self. Punningly and unsentimentally, one could say that nature is not "red" but "well-read" in tooth and claw, "well-informed" by the wisdom which spurns violence beyond the necessities of survival. In the animate world this wisdom is disowned by the human species alone, especially if not exclusively by its non-aboriginal societies.

Whether regarded as representing materiality or non-human life, the bombs in their newspaper-borne flight back to the source of newspapers, printing machines, dramatize instructively the faithfulness of self's self-imaging in these arenas of manifestation. For faithful self-images alone can return with the sure instinct of homing pigeons to the source of self-imaging śakti, self, nobly represented by the rotary machines.

Menacing as the bombs are in their power of multiplication and mobility, their self-sameness in plurality is a striking encapsulation of advaita; as is the unobstructedness of their flight in its evocation of the idea that singular self can only encounter the appearance, never the reality, of not-self. No density of self-obscuration can entirely shut out the light of self-consciousness; but it is sin enough to try to do so.

We can do without those bombs.

6

In their newspaper-clothed incarnation, however, the bombs represent to me nothing less than the grace of Sadguru Śrī Ramaṇa; because, unenduringly yet undoubtedly, they blessed me with an experience of the death of ego, the dissolution of the idea that I was only a given body, mind, personality, biography, etc; and, as promised by Ramaṇa, without the slightest sense of any loss of the reality and luminosity of self-consciousness. The experience didn't survive the dream, but its promise does.

7

The child form of the dreamer enclosed (but with a skylight qualification) in the machine room steeped in the symbolism of procreativity is a rudely biological representation of selfhood, a vivid picture of "dehātmabuddhi," of the presumption that one is but a given body, mind, etc.: ego in short. One would expect the death of ego in this setting to provoke loud parental lamentation, for what is born and dies is ego: self is unborn, undying. What is heard, instead, is a reaffirmation of love in a feminine voice. Whose voice is this? And for whom is love reaffirmed?

She who speaks is my mother as self, imaged by all forms and not only by the beloved form dissolved by death eight years ago. Love is affirmed for a form which permits a nightmare to run its course and resolve into self-knowledge; for a child willing to suffer the shock of initiation into the limitlessness of home.

"We were afraid you might not come back home" is what my mother had said when I asked her, some years before she died, why I hadn't been sent to Śrī Ramaṇa's hermitage for a "darśana" of the sage, considering I was all of thirteen years of age when he left the body. Hindu women fear that their young sons might renounce the world under the influence of holy men, and guard them against this possibility. My mother need not have worried. The world is still very much with me, a poor householder though I have been. Śrī Ramaṇa in any case asks us not to renounce the world, but to see it as ourselves.

The movements of my newspaper office dream reconcile the claims of reproduction and renunciation, form and formlessness; and I accept the cinematic experience as a gift of initiatory surreality from both mother and sage and offer salutations to both; indistinguishably.

8

When it was reported to Śrī Rāmakṛṣṇa Paramahaṃsa that a certain disciple of his had started quite unnecessarily to learn English, the Master said "Now he will start whistling, and wear boots!".[2] The purity of Śrī Rāmakṛṣṇa's heart would not have permitted him to notice that that humorous portrait of the Englishman in India in the nineteenth century is a devastating indictment of colonial authority: of its racially heavyfooted (boots) and culturally vacuous (whistling) disregard of native Indian sensibility.

Authoritarian boots and trivializing whistling (my partiality for whistling is troubled by the adjective, but let it pass) are costly caricatures of qualities which native English speaking manifests impressively easily most of the time: the power of gestureless, concentrated, self-confidence, and the authority of deflating deadpan humor. And this combination of qualities dramatizes what I think is the very essence of language: the simultaneous demonstration and disavowal of causal capability. In different yet related ways, British moral vulnerability and militant Gandhian non-violence did manage to exhibit something of this truth of language, the holocaust of India's partition and its continuing aftermath notwithstanding.

9

En route to Oxford on my first visit to England as a graduate student in 1964, on the train from Dover to Victoria station, I had noticed that everyone was reading a newspaper and no one was talking. I actually thought the silence was a ritual of mourning for a departed soul. More than a quarter of a century later, I can now see that that is what it was, symbolically and fundamentally; and not only that.

The silence of the newspaper readers dramatized the soundlessness of the written or the printed word, not excluding the powerfully persuasive print of newspapers, thus proclaiming the truth that human communication is unachievable without causal self-restraint. Newspaper-veiled commuters mourned the demise of causal prodigality, and silently savored the joy of its communicative rebirth.

It was train again from Victoria to Paddington, and from Paddington to Oxford; where, over the next few years, precisely this feature of human communication formed the focus of my discussions with Peter, now Sir Peter, Strawson, my supervisor at University College. By way of acknowledging guru ṛṇa, I would like here to express my profound gratitude to Sir Peter Strawson for introducing me to issues in contemporary philosophy of language which have been starting points of a journey towards advaita which I find as baffling as I had found that silent train journey from Dover to Victoria station. Amazingly, the newspaper office dream encapsulates the salient features of this journey.

Printing machines and newspaper-borne missiles are powerfully suggestive of the idea that human communication is a stirring up and streaming forth of causal energies, a targeting of audiences by suitably efficacious utterances produced and launched by speakers. That this is appearance not reality is suggested by the non-violent impact of the communicative missiles on their target;[3] and by inquiry. For if causal efficaciousness were central to communication, how is it that we do not lose faith in communication despite the fact that in normal circumstances our utterances manifestly lack the power to cause our audiences to believe or do what they represent? On the contrary, human communication derives its credibility from the disavowal of manipulative intent poignantly implicit in the causally unthreatening form of linguistic utterances.[4] The face-to-face and hands-off character of speaking in general is itself such a disavowal, like the essential soundlessness of the written word (The strongest men speak without grappling with their hearers. Even noisy old-style rotary machines produce silent print).

A difficulty presents itself here. If speakers and audiences were in essence, and not merely in appearance, other than one another, the disavowal of causal aim in communication would be an unresolvable paradox, otherness being causality's irresistible nourishment. The paradox resolves itself only on the non-dualist assumption that it is singular self-consciousness which sets up in its play of self-imaging the apparent duality of speakers and audiences, which it then unmasks as appearance and not reality by demonstrating the possibility of establishing a communicative relationship between speakers and audiences without causal agency; indeed by demonstrating the impossibility of establishing such a relationship merely causally, dualistically. And I refer here to normal, not telepathic, communication.

10

Oxford never fails to surprise. On a recent visit I discovered that the university's oldest church, St Mary's, has now a mural of Mahātmā Gandhi: a small figure seated in the cross-legged posture, wearing what look like John Lennon spectacles, with upraised hands in abhaya mudrā offering a double boon of fearlessness in a bold extension of conventional iconography. The right hand assures us of the unavailingness of violence in communication, and the left hand of the revolutionary possibilities that are open to non-violence in human evolution.

Equally plausibly, the double-voting upraised hands can be seen as highlighting Gandhi's rejection of exclusivist identities. He was a Hindu, but insisted that he was simultaneously also a Muslim, Christian, Jew, Buddhist, Jaina, etc.: a believer in the truth of all faiths. He loved fellow human beings as himself, and had no difficulty in honoring their deepest concerns as his own. Perhaps his mural in St Mary's draws attention to the neglected inclusivist dimension of Christ's teaching that man does not live by bread alone, but by every word that proceeds from the mouth of God; i.e. that we are adequately nourished by nothing less than the full range of truth's manifestation.

A non-dualist Church of Ātman-Brahman Mary — Godhead, no mere saint—would be a generous kitchen offering without exclusivist denial the full range of truth's cuisine to spiritually hungry humanity, in accordance with Christ's own nutritional manifesto.

The words "Man does not live by bread alone, but by every word that proceeds from the mouth of God" were uttered by Christ in response to Satan's demand that he prove his divinity by turning stones into bread through the exercise of some manipulatively miraculous causal agency. Words that proceed from the mouth of God are all words that attain to communication through a disavowal of causal agency, revealing the non-duality of speakers and hearers, self and apparent not-self: thus inviting us to live ethically and ecologically sensitively by loving one another and the world as ourselves. We don't, of course, cussedly. We have ears but do not hear the non-dualist good news broadcast by every spoken word in communication.

11

Svāmī Vivekānanda was in Kashmir towards the end of his life, but his heart was heavy even in that paradise on earth. Large-hearted though he was, he felt tormented by the fact that successive invaders had desecrated and destroyed countless sacred images of Hinduism's Gods and Goddesses and pulled down Hindu temples and built mosques over their ruins. Unable to bear the burden of this humiliating testimony of history, Vivekānanda poured out his anguish at the feet of the Divine Mother in a Kālī temple. "How could you let this happen, Mother, why did you permit this desecration?" he asked despairingly. Svāmījī has himself recorded all this, and reports[5] that Kālī whispered in his heart the following reply to his question:

"What is it to you, Vivekānanda, if the invader breaks my images. Do you protect me, or do I protect you?" Only the revelatory authority of that chastisement and consolation can heal the wounds of history from which Hinduism suffers.

A testing time has come.

12

Injured Hindu pride is being morally bullied and cajoled to perceive a sixteenth century mosque in Ayodhyā, the Bābarī mosque, as the very embodiment of otherness; sheer, indissoluble, otherness. As advaita's Waterloo.

The mosque stands on a high and wide mound which Hindu piety identifies as the area somewhere within which Śrī Rāma was born datelessly long ago; and also as the area somewhere within which was situated his wife's, Śrī Sītā's, Kitchen. Now the existence of a mosque within this ambience of sacredness need not as such hurt Hindu pride; it can easily be seen as proof of the accommodatingness of Hinduism's spiritual sensibility.

Indeed, in normal circumstances, the topographical inclusion of a mosque within the sacred precincts of Rāma's birthplace and Sītā's Kitchen would convey a message of profound and special spiritual significance, and I will return to this theme. The times, however, are not normal in India today, communally speaking. Islamic secessionism in Kashmir and imitative Sikh secessionism in Punjab, assisted by successfully seceded Pakistan, have yielded a frightening Hindu backlash in the country which enables Hindu fundamentalism to use communal memory of old historical wrongs to reap rich political profits for itself. The chief art of Indian civilization is the ability to turn worldly adversity to spiritual advantage. Attempts to right the wrongs of the past by wrongs of the present will be the death of this art; and possibly also of Indian civilization.

Politically and communicatively powerful Hindu organizations are claiming, without the authority of any body of extant archeological or literary evidence, secular or sacred, which cannot be seriously questioned, that the Bābarī mosque in Ayodhyā stands precisely at the spot where Rāma was born and where there once stood a temple commemorating his birth. This temple, it is alleged, was destroyed at the behest of Bābar, the founder of the Mughal empire which symbolized the pinnacle of Islamic power in India; and that a mosque was built at its site, incorporating some of the materials and structures of the destroyed temple which were suitably defaced for the purpose; but not entirely, so as to let them bear the humiliating testimony of the conquest of Hindu India by Muslim forces and the forcible conversion of

Hindus to Islam. And all this at a commanding height in one of the holiest of Hindu shrines, the capital city of God-incarnate Rāma's kingdom on earth.

Conquered, cannibalized, converted. This is the message of humiliation which the Hindu psyche is being forced to regard the Bābarī mosque as broadcasting ceaselessly from the summit of Ayodhyā across more than four centuries.

"Relocate the mosque somewhere else, although it deserves to be destroyed. And reconstruct at the liberated site the original temple, or build a new one, commemorating the birth and birthplace of Rāma." This is the vindictive demand of Hindu assertiveness today in Ayodhyā, unworthy of Hinduism and unnecessary for piety, which has plunged India into a major political crisis and a communal convulsion which has already taken hundreds of lives.

But it is not only Hindu pride that is hurt.

13

It is claimed by Hindu organizations agitating for the relocation of the Bābarī mosque that on the night of December 22, or during the early hours of December 23, 1949, images of Śrī Rāma and Śrī Sītā miraculously manifested inside the mosque. All evidence available points to the contrary; not to a miracle but to trespass, to the fact that the images were placed inside the mosque surreptitiously by zealots who broke into it at night for the purpose. Fearing the outbreak of violence in the communally surcharged atmosphere of the time (barely two years after the holocaust of India's partition), district authorities put a lock on the mosque, forbidding Muslim prayers in it.

Thirty-seven years later, in 1986, an avowedly secular Congress government anxious to woo Hindu voters caused a pliant judge to order the breaking open of the lock on the mosque, but not the removal of the images: opening the floodgates of fundamentalism.

This forcible conversion of a mosque into a temple, not in the years immediately following the trauma of partition, but decades later, and with the apparent connivance of government, has deeply wounded Muslim sensibility in India. Politically and communicatively powerful Muslim organizations have not lagged behind their Hindu counterparts in working up the faithful into a state of frenzy over this fait accompli. It is true that no court of law has as yet validated the Hindu claim to the site, but the mosque *is* a functioning Hindu temple, and the symbolism of this has not been lost on Indian Muslims: that Hindu hegemonism is capable of converting India into a Hindu State in which non-Hindu minorities will be less equal than the Hindu majority.

Ayodhyā today presents an aspect of otherness to Muslims which is as stark as the aspect of otherness under which Hindus see the Bābarī mosque towering over the city of Rāma.

Hindus are not allowed by fundamentalist rhetoric to recall that it was precisely during the sixteenth century, when the Bābarī mosque was built, that devotion to Rāma found a tidal expression all over northern India which has never ebbed; that they have been well protected by Sītā and have no cause to grieve inconsolably over Islamic iconoclasm's destructive denial of the truth of image worship, for this truth flourishes all over India.

Likewise, Indian Muslims are not allowed by fundamentalist Islamic rhetoric to engage in insightful interpretation[6] of their relationship not only to the Ayodhyā mosque, but to the reality of post-partition India as a whole, which has so far vehemently refused to declare itself a Hindu State, its demographic status as a massive Hindu-majority area notwithstanding; and despite the provocation of Pakistan and Bangladesh — Muslim-majority areas which seceded from India in 1947—being Islamic theocracies.

The sheer and un-self-restrained causality of bigotry's oratory preempts any dialogue with it. And in the absence of dialogue, its spiritual superficiality remains unexposed, making it difficult for argument — spiritual or secular — to make much headway with the faithful. Thoughtful Hindus and Muslims are marginalized as bombs of hatred manifest in the sky and terrify fledgeling Indian democracy as they move towards its ancestral home of spiritual catholicity and wisdom, threatening to destroy both progeny and ancestry.

I had to go to Ayodhyā.

14

In the temple town of Ayodhyā in the Faizabad district of Uttar Pradesh, high above the eastern bank of the Sarayū river, the three-domed and three-arched Bābarī mosque stands conspicuously on the north-eastern corner of the Ramkot mound (taking its name after a fortress called Ramkot which once commanded the height).

I stood in front of the main arch of the mosque and noticed the carved lotuses and pitchers on the small pillars supporting it at the bottom, and the hexagonal tantric motifs on the walls above the arches and other unmistakably Hindu[7] features of the structure. There could be little doubt that sacred components of a Hindu temple (or a cognate Buddhist or Jaina shrine) had been used in the construction of the mosque in the sixteenth century (1528/29).

Perhaps an existing temple had been destroyed to construct the mosque at its site, using some of its materials. Perhaps the mosque was built over the ruins of a temple destroyed by Islamic iconoclasm long before Bābar's time. Perhaps the materials were brought from some other site to the Ramkot area and the Bābarī mosque built with their aid on vacant land. Whatever be the precise historical truth of this matter, the fact remains that the mosque owes its existence to the despoliation of structures sacred to Indian spirituality and does not hide this fact; adding insult to injury, says my wounded Hindu pride.

The child in me grieved bitterly as I stood in front of the mosque thinking these thoughts.

Soon, however, the adult in me awakened to the reality of the images of Rāma and Sītā and other deities in the sanctum sanctorum of the house of Allāh; to the fact of stealthy trespass with intent which converted the Bābarī mosque into a Rāma temple more than forty years ago; to the fact that the chanting of the names of Rāma and Sītā — essential nourishment for my Hindu soul — had been used to silence nearly half a millennium's call to Islamic prayer; to the fact that Muslims were not allowed to come anywhere near the mosque under siege, which no doubt was an addition of insult to the injury caused to their pride by the forcible conversion of a mosque into a temple in secular India.

15

Religious exclusivism had converted a medieval building into a terrorist time-bomb which was likely to explode at any moment in the face of secular morality and spiritual catholicity, grievously injuring India's distinctive identity in the modern world as a civilization which sought to cherish both secularism and spirituality. The child and the adult turned in desperation to Śrī Ramaṇa.

Help was at hand. I opened my eyes. My attention was drawn to what I had not noticed the first time around, a signboard of quite contemporary origin which said in Hindi 'Janmasthān Sītā-kī-rasoi,' i.e. 'Birthplace (Rāma's) Sītā's Kitchen.' My eyes and heart were opened to a neglected but crucial aspect of the Ayodhyā controversy.

Media accounts of the controversy had made no mention of the fact that the Bābarī mosque was located in a zone of the Ramkot mound which was revered by Hindu devotees not *only* as Rāma's birth-place, but *also* as Sītā's Kitchen.[8] The voluminous mosque-baiting propaganda of Hindu indignation was also devoid of any reference to Sītā's Kitchen.

Bitterness sought in a male supremacist way to commemorate Rāma and banish Sītā from memory; even as the male supremacist citizenry of Ayodhyā in the Rāmāyaṇa had crowned Rāma and caused the banishment of Sītā. A script of tragedy deeply encoded in consciousness was demanding to be replayed.[9]

The Hindi phrase 'Sītā-kī-rasoi' has a resonance which the English translation 'Sītā's Kitchen' does not have for me: an ambience of domesticity and divinity which happily includes the pious notion of an actual kitchen where Godhead-incarnate Sītā cooked delicious and nutritious food for the Rāghava household, but stretches all the way beyond that architectural idea to the archetypal notion of the earth as the Divine Mother's laboratory of manifestation and field of nourishment for all self-images of self.

The sacred words 'Birth-place Sītā's Kitchen' posted above the main arch of the mosque held the time-bomb in self-realizing self-restraint, and formed a banner headline without whose guidance it would be impossible to read that stone-story as revealing anything but shame. I took those words as Guru Ramaṇa's gift of a saving mantra to embattled Indian civilization in ironically "un-battle-able" Ayodhyā. It is more than a year since my eyes were opened to that magic inscription in crude paint, and my mind and heart will continue to meditate on the meaning of that inscription long after the Ayodhyā dispute is resolved, as I hope, by the grace of Rāma and Sītā and Ramaṇa, it will be.

The element 'Sītā's Kitchen' in the compound phrase "Birth-place Sītā's Kitchen" can be read as an answer written against the item "Birthplace" in a column of questions regarding Rāma or any manifest form, avatāric or ordinary. And the Sītā whose kitchen is also the birthplace of Rāma is only in manifestation his consort; in reality she is Mahālakṣmī, Godhead, Self; and Sītā's Kitchen is the entire field of her self-imaging Śakti, powerfully represented by the earth.

It is on earth, in the embrace of the Divine Mother, that all are born, all creatures great and small; all forms manifest, noble or evil; and all are nourished. I have no doubt at all that at least the northern portion of the Ramkot mound in Ayodhyā must have been in antiquity a sacred fertility grove, an aboriginal shrine of the Divine Mother which acquired the name "Sītā's Kitchen" during the Ramāyaṇa age without the slightest loss of significance.

The Ramkot zone sheltering the Bābarī Mosque is *as a whole* Sītā's Kitchen, and also every part and portion of it. Any number of kitchen shrines can be established there. One such is a platform outside the mosque's northern wall, whose deities are a rolling board and a rolling pin; powerful symbols of generativeness and humble apparatus of bread-making, decidedly of aboriginal authenticity in conception.

Likewise, the zone as a whole is Rāma's birthplace; and every part and portion of it and every point on its surface. Any number of birthplace shrines can be established there. One such is a platform — the Rām Chabootra — near the mosque's main entrance.

And the Bābarī mosque could also be regarded as a birthplace shrine; it could always have been so regarded, even before the images of Rāma and Sītā were stealthily installed inside it, and without the necessity of that act of trespass and appropriation. Because the mosque falls within the sacred birthplace and kitchen area, and every structure situated within that area is simultaneously a birthplace shrine of Rāma and a kitchen shrine of Sītā; with or without the benefit of the installation and consecration and worship of sacred images inside the structure.

The insistence that the sanctum sanctorum of the mosque is the precise and exclusive place of Rāma's birth is blasphemy, not faith; and of course it is not theology or archeology or history. It is not blasphemous to hold a zone, a finite surface, to be the birthplace area, every part and portion of it; because such a zone, so understood, would be a lucid image of omnipresence; Rāma's, Godhead's, Self's omnipresence. What is blasphemous is the denial of omnipresence by imposing the task of imaging it exclusively on any one spot in the zone area. This is what Hindu narrow-mindedness is doing Hinduism-denyingly by accusing the Bābarī mosque of standing on the supposedly singular spot marking Rāma's birth.

The spiritual motifs carved on the pillars and stones of the Bābarī mosque are common to Hinduism, Buddhism, and Jainism, and the location of the mosque in the sacred kitchen zone of Ramkot draws pointed attention to the kinship of these traditions with aboriginal spirituality. In thus drawing attention to the coherent spiritual universe of aboriginality, Hinduism, Buddhism, and Jainism, the mosque makes a stupendous contribution to Indian self-knowledge. Ought such a teacher be allowed to be banished by ungrateful pupils?

The apparent intractable otherness of the mosque as a reminder of historical humiliation is overcome in the intimacy of kinship-establishing self-knowledge to which that sentinel of Ramkot awakens the grieving pride of Hinduism.

Not only that. The Bābarī mosque's medieval trespass into the kitchen area dramatizes the entry of Sūfism into the corpus of Indian mysticism. Indeed, the cognateness of Abrahamic mysticism in general, and not only Sūfism, with Hindu, aboriginal, and Buddhist mysticism, is powerfully suggested by the continuity of the mosque's inner space[10] of objectlessness with the void of the kitchen zone, which is continuous with the sphericality of the earth and with surrounding emptiness. And this continuity, along with the autonomy of each area of emptiness, is deeply evocative of ahiṃsā or non-violence, the virtue emphasized centrally by Jainism and savingly by Gandhi in our annihilationist age.

Indian spiritual self-knowledge cannot become self-realization without encounter with non-Indian spiritual traditions, and without sharing space and time with them. Held in topographical and historical embrace by the birthplace and kitchen zone of Ayodhyā, the Bābarī mosque is evidence not of Hindu humiliation but of its venturesome sādhanā of self-realization.

The apparent insurmountable otherness of the mosque as a representative of exclusivism is softened by the realization which the interloper in Ramkot forces upon nativist Indian spirituality, namely, that its universe has been widened by Islam's presence in India.

But what about the interloping images in the mosque?

The later nawabs of Avadh were avid patrons of Hindu temples in the entire provincial region of which Ayodhyā is a part; and especially Rāma and Kṛṣṇa bhakti flourished under their rule. It should be possible for Muslims, and not only Muslims, to see the images implanted in the Bābarī mosque as representing the hospitableness of Islamic rule in Avadh to Hindu spirituality; and as reflecting the lodgment of Rāma and Sītā, Kṛṣṇa and Rādhā, in many a Sūfī heart; and of their names in the singing voice of great Muslim masters of classical Hindustānī music.

16

The Bābarī edifice is a testifying tree which bears the flowers of nearly five hundred years of Islamic piety, and of nearly fifty years of Hindu bhakti. It could have grown only in the sacred soil of Sītā's Kitchen, and cannot be transplanted anywhere else. Certainly the tree bears thorns too, thorns of medieval and modern vandalism. But it can give shade to pilgrims weary of hatred in the name of the sacred for at least another half a millennium. Cutting it down would be ominous for life and civilization on earth.

Hindus and Muslims must forgive each other's trespasses in Ayodhyā, if they wish their trespasses against each other all over India to be forgiven.

That Christian thought takes my mind to Oxford and St Mary's church and the Gandhi mural's double-voting upraised arms. With one raised arm Gandhi votes for the status quo to be preserved in relation to the Bābarī mosque in Ayodhyā; and with the other he votes for a sacred grove to be established in front of the mosque by the ādivāsīs and harijans of India as a kitchen shrine of Sītā, within which could be accommodated a separate birthplace shrine of Rāma.

Or could it be that Gandhi's upraised arms in the mural are a despairing gesture, an anticipation of annihilation?

17

Annihilationism (the readiness to destroy all life and civilization on earth) is the highest stage of development of dualism, if one may be permitted thus to update Lenin's epigram regarding imperialism and capitalism. Dualism is the conviction that self and not-self are everywhere pitted against one another. Individual human beings against one another and against human collectivities. Human collectivities against one another and against individual human beings, living species against one another. The human species against all other living species. All life against matter, all existence against nothingness. Sooner rather than later, the flickering light of existence is going to be snuffed out by nothingness. So why not advance the hour of annihilation? This is the temptation of annihilation, dualism's despairing destructiveness now unfurling in all societies on an unprecedented scale.[11]

In India's inner life, however, dualism has been deeply rebutted in a variety of ways by aboriginal spirituality, Hinduism, Buddhism and Jainism. Ayodhyā's heritage of Hindu, Buddhist, and Jaina traditions is well known. And if my faith in the aboriginality —and, therefore, timeless antiquity—of Sītā's Kitchen is not delusion, dualism's annihilationist darkness cannot prevail against Ayodhya's comprehensive arsenal of light.

Hindus and Muslims must not allow this light to be dimmed by failing to resolve the Bābarī crisis non-dualistically, i.e. without either side experiencing a sense of humiliation at the hands of the "other."

18

My faith in the aboriginality of Sītā's Kitchen in Ayodhyā is not only supported by the undeniable connotations of generativity carried by the name of the place. It is strengthened by the Rāmāyaṇa itself.

In a profoundly revelatory episode,[12] ādivāsī — aboriginal — king Guha and Rāma embrace each other in a gesture of perfect equality, letting us into the secret that the truth of Guha and the truth of Rāma are one.

What is the truth of Guha, of aboriginality? The truth of Guha is the truth of the earth as the Divine Mother's kitchen, the truth of her nourishing care of all her creatures who are forms of manifestation of herself, of primal energy. At least this.

And what is the truth of Rāma? Invoking the authority of the Adhyātma Rāmāyaṇa[13] and the Yoga Vāsiṣṭha[14] and the authority of Śrī Ramaṇa Maharṣi, and in the light of my own reading of the epic, I submit that the truth of Rāma is the truth of advaita, non-duality; the truth of singular self-consciousness and its cinematic field of self-imaging śakti which is saṃsāra. At least this.

The truth of aboriginality and the truth of advaita are one. To banish all doubts in regard to this sacred identity, let us remind ourselves that it is Guha who instructs a fellow-aboriginal to row Rāma, Sītā, and Lakṣmaṇa across the waters of a river from one shore to another[15]: a function which in its deepest meaning is attributable only to divinity. The episode, no doubt, also encodes aboriginality's dateless trusteeship and transportation of the Rāmāyaṇa story across the river of time.

Rāma and Sītā being one in selfhood, the identity of the truth of aboriginality and advaita could not in antiquity have been more pointedly expressed than by the establishment of a grove of generativity bearing the name "Sītā's Kitchen." I maintain in faith that the mound of controversy in contemporary Ayodhyā was this grove of hope, and still can be.

It is the firm conviction of the Śrī Rāmānuja tradition of Vaiṣṇava bhakti, into which my mother and her ancestors were born, that the episode of Sītā's banishment is an undevout kaliyuga interpolation in the Rāmāyaṇa; that the original story ended with the coronation of Rāma and Sītā in Ayodhyā after their victorious return from Laṅkā. I remember trying to defend the authenticity of the banishment episode in an argument with my mother. "I am impressed by your bhakti, Ramu, not your arguments," is what she said by way of demanding deeper thought from me on the matter; and not dismissively, I am sure. I think I can defend my position better now; not unaided by bhakti, though, nor without restorative presumptuousness. The following readings of Rāmāyaṇa episodes are dedicated with gratitude to my mother and her paurāṇika father, Chakravartī Rājagopālācharī.

The Rāmāyaṇa begins with a narration of ecological violation.[16] One of a pair of krauñca birds in love-play on the branch of a tree is felled by a hunter's arrow, in clear violation of the code of ecologically honorable hunting. The horrified observer of this scene is the author of the Rāmāyaṇa himself, sage Vālmīki. He curses the hunter angrily, harshly condemning him to a life of ceaseless, restless, wandering. The sage, however, is soon filled with remorse for his un-sage-like act of cursing, and for the harshness of his curse; but he is equally fascinated by the metrical music of his cursing words. Creator Brahmā himself materializes to allay the sage's anxiety, and asks him to set the Rāmāyaṇa story to verse in the haunting meter of his curse.

I suggest that this opening episode of the epic legislates that ecological violation cannot be too harshly condemned, and is a narrative determinant which drives the epic on remorselessly to the eventual separation of Rāma and Sītā as the price which even the divine couple have to pay for the ecological violation implicit in the killing of the demon deer Mārīca by Rāma at Sītā's instigation. It was necessary to kill Mārīca, but not for food or clothing, as Rāma, Sītā and Lakṣmaṇa were not in need of these at the time Mārīca appeared in their hermitage. But such need is the only justification for hunting! Although unavoidable, the killing of Mārīca is also unavoidably unecological. Mārīca is separated from a possible deer mate at the level of manifestation. And so, again at the level of manifestation, Rāma and Sītā have to separate soon after reuniting, like the krauñca birds.

In its passage through time, the aboriginal trusteeship of the Rāmāyaṇa seems to have passed into the hands of chauvinists and courtiers of exploitative city states. The ecologically educative separation of Rāma and Sītā by mutual consent became distorted into the sexist banishment of Sītā by Rāma for suspected infidelity in Laṅkā. This ancient distortion encourages today's chauvinist and ecologically insensitive politicians of little faith to see in the Bābarī Masjid the violation of Sītā and to seek its banishment from Ayodhyā, and the construction in its place of a dualistically divided temple dedicated to Rāma without Sītā.

I hold fast to my belief in faith that after Sītā's recourse to the forests across the Sarayū, Rāma and Guha established an aboriginal grove of generativity in the heart of Ayodhyā, which was undoubtedly both a birthplace shrine of Rāma and a kitchen shrine of Sītā: the indivisibility sanctified by the deity forms of a rolling board and a rolling pin.

20

It is said that the Buddha was born on a night of the full moon, and that his enlightenment and death also occurred on nights of the full moon. It is also said that Mahāvīra was born on a moonless night, and that his enlightenment and death also occurred on moonless nights. The symbolism of these beliefs is powerfully instructive.

The sun of upaniṣadic advaita was no doubt deeply obscured by clouds of ignorance and inequity in the age of the Buddha and Mahāvīra. And the trusteeship of the Rāmāyaṇa and the Mahābhārata must have begun to pass from aboriginal and enlightened hands to careerists and charlatans. Nihilist teachers of awesome ascetic eminence like the Ājīvikas[17] Ajita Keśakambalin and Makkhali Gośāla, of whose contemporaneity with Mahāvīra and the Buddha we know, must have dominated the intellectual life of an age whose self-confidence and even self-consciousness must have begun to atrophy in the absence of a living contact with advaita.

The full moon represents the power of illumined mind which, in the form of the Buddha, came to the aid of that sunless age: teaching advaita through compassion and in the light of reason drawing attention to emptiness which held all existence in its embrace without itself being a competing entity among entities, identifiable also as all-upholding dhamma and nirvāṇa's non-entitative reality beyond relativity.

The Buddha could have identified emptiness or nirvāṇa or dhamma with ātman or self, but did not do so because the atrophying self-consciousness of that age would have taken self to mean ego or body or mind, with disastrous consequences for his mission of compassion.

The Buddha's teaching of the inter-relatedness of all evanescent items and orders of not-self-hood, and their situatedness within non-entitative emptiness or nirvāṇa or dhamma, is also wholly consonant with aboriginality's vision of the vibrant interdependence of all forms of life and their location within the nourishing embrace of Mother Earth.

Nights of the full moon awaken the forest of life to a celebration of interdependence, to a middle ground between the burdensomeness of toil and the inertia of sleep. The truth of eros is not absent in Kṛṣṇa's incarnation as the Buddha, it merely becomes translated as the irresistibility of enlightenment.

And on a moonless night, when, symbolically, neither the sun of self-realization nor the full moon of enlightenment is at hand, we have to walk on the earth very gently, lest we hurt fellow living beings. Ahiṃsā is born, Mahāvīra is born. Ecology, the implicit self-restraint of non-human forms of life in their adventure of survival, becomes self-conscious ahiṃsā and those who practice ahiṃsā in all spheres of living are "Mahāvīra": great heroes.

Each vulnerable living being, frightened in the moonless darkness of the night of ignorance and cynicism, can attain to self-sufficiency — kaivalya — through the practice of ahiṃsā: implicit or self-conscious and ceaselessly vigilant. Even a moonless night manifests distant stars, themselves suns, self-luminous, alone and autonomous. The humblest organism can hope to realize the self-luminosity of those stars. There is plurality and diversity in that realization of kaivalya, no duality.

In its celebration of self-restraint, Jaina ahiṃsā pays a profound tribute to aboriginal humanity's moral and metaphysical continuity with other orders of life, and with the processes of materiality whose lawfulness is witness to the causal self-restraint of these processes.

Vegetarianism is Jainism's unique contribution to civilization, and a future universal life-style of humanity. It is a kitchen of ahiṃsā within aboriginality's, Sītā's, larger kitchen of advaita: and promised steady expansion by it, but not prematurely or self-righteously.

21

Here is the Vinayapiṭaka text, the 'Bhaddavaggiyavatthu',[18] the canonical record of an occurrence in the life of the Buddha which is speculatively explored and expanded in the dialogical narrative of this book along the lines of the preceding meditations.

(1) And the Blessed One, after having dwelt at Benares as long as He thought fit, went forth to Uruvela. And the Blessed One left the road and went to a certain grove; having gone there, and having entered it, He sat down at the foot of a tree. At that time there was a party of thirty friends, rich young men, who were sporting in that same grove together with their wives. One of them had no wife; for him they had provided a harlot. Now while they did not pay attention and were indulging in their sports, that harlot took up the articles belonging to them, and ran away.

(2) Then those companions, doing service to their friend, went in search of that woman; and roaming about that grove, they saw the Blessed One sitting at the foot of a tree. Seeing Him they went to the place where the Blessed One was; having approached Him, they said to the Blessed One: "Pray, Lord, has the Blessed One seen a woman passing by?"

"What have you to do, young men, with the woman?"

"We were sporting, Lord, in the grove, thirty friends, rich young men, together with our wives. One of us had no wife; for him we had provided a harlot. Now Lord, while we did not pay attention, and were indulging in our sports, that harlot has taken up the articles belonging to us, and has run away. Therefore, Lord, we companions doing service to our friend, go in search of that woman and roam about this grove."

(3) "Now what think you, young men? Which would be better for you, that you should go in search of a woman, or that you should go in search of yourselves?"[19]

"That, Lord, would be better for us, that we should go in search of ourselves."

"If so, young men, sit down, I will preach to you the truth, (Dharma)"

The rich young companions replied: "Yes, Lord," and respectfully saluted the Blessed One, and sat down near him.

(4) Then the Blessed One preached to them . . .

(5) And having seen the truth . . . the venerable persons received the Upasampadā Ordination.

There is in the above text a two and a half thousand years old and yet quite contemporary-sounding cheekiness to the young men's conversation with the Buddha which makes their apparent sudden conversion to the Dhamma seem quite implausible. I would like to think the cheekiness springs not only from youthful irreverence and aristocratic arrogance, but also from exposure to the thought and influence of the likes of such nihilist masters of the age as Makkhali Gośāla and Ajita Keśakambalin.

I know of no historical grounds for supposing that these wizards of id might have known each other and jointly dared moral and metaphysical self-confidence to justify itself in public debate.

Nor is there any basis in extant historical evidence to suggest that the Buddha and Mahāvīra ever met, or that there was any occasion for them jointly to confront nihilist defiance.

However, in the speculative narrative which follows, the nihilists and the sages are brought together by a symposium to which the former summon the latter and also the whole 'Bhaddavaggiya' gang of outraged rank, Brāhmaṇical philosophers and paurāṇikas and a crowd of high and low born citizens of the land, friends and foes.

The aim of the symposium is to debate the issues arising out of the Buddha's advice to aristocracy to seek self and not revenge against an escaped and thieving slave: an ādivāsī girl called Ananyā who has taken refuge in the Buddha, and who claims she stole the valuables of her masters to make an offering of them to Sītā at her kitchen shrine in Ayodhyā as a gesture of atonement for humanity's violation of the integrity of consciousness and the ecology of nature.

What is at stake is the honor of Indian spiritual traditions[20] and the fate of life and civilization on earth. What is offered is a testimony of faith and inquiry.

SĪTĀ'S KITCHEN

I

The Buddha is in a forest near Vārāṇasī, pacing up and down in a clearing in the forest, savoring the peace of the radical victory over craving that he has won. A scene for the Gods, liberation for the earth and all her creatures from the thraldom of becoming. Precisely at that point in time, somewhere else in the same forest, a group of revelers are lost in their pleasures. They are the aristocracy, the beautiful people of the great cities of the time: Vaiśālī, Vārāṇasī, Śrāvastī, etc. The only person in that group who does not have a partner is a slave girl whose responsibility it is to look after the valuables of the lovers lost in their ecstasies.

Think of the powerful beautiful instructive scene. The Buddha's solitary, leonine, immersion in the light of freedom and the bondage of the couples to fleeting pleasures, impartially witnessed perhaps by the self-same full moon. Can a Satyajit Ray capture this mysterious similarity and difference between nirvāṇa and saṃsāra in a film version of the Vinayapiṭaka text, the 'Bhaddavaggiyavatthu'[21] (translatable as "Something Noble"), which tells this story?

The slave woman runs away with the valuables — jewelry, ornaments — of her owners. Surely the selfish lovers deserve this! To leave anyone out of the sphere of love and justice is to invite the wrath of retribution. The lovers awaken from their stupor of indulgence, and finding their valuables gone along with their slave custodian, they are furious beyond measure. A great shot for a great film. Beautiful selfish men and women, disheveled hair, ugly wrath on their faces, self-righteous horror at the way they think their trust has been betrayed by a mere slave girl. A search for the thief is launched. No doubt not only on foot, but on horseback too. Perhaps elephants too are pressed into service. The terrified face of the girl caught intermittently by moonlight as she runs, runs, runs; falling down, getting up, running and falling and running again.

The search party destroys the tranquillity of the forest, disturbs the ecology of the "araṇya," literally "that which cannot be battled": a metaphor of self, a promise and a place of peace. The Buddha walking up and down in one corner of the forest; the woman in flight in the deep recesses of the forest; and the enraged destructive aristocrats determined to hunt her down and yet mysteriously driven by destiny closer and closer to where the Lord himself is. Work for cameras in helicopters and hope for the unenlightened.

The film loses sight of the hunted woman now, but discovers the Buddha in moonlit, ethereal, close-ups. Not quite the face at once, but only the hem of the kaṣāya, saffron robe, the blessed feet, hand in jñāna mudrā, gesture of gnosis; and then the sāṃsāric, worldly, roar of the search party as it invades the territory of the Tathāgata. Haughty men and women discourteously accosting the Lord. We only see the back of his head, *gheraoing*[22] him soon are these representatives of high birth. In a chorus of voices they ask the Buddha if the ungrateful wretch has passed that way; if he has heard her cries; if he has any information at all regarding her which can help them catch and punish her suitably. Torch-bearers close in, and the whole effrontery is made sadly visible.

But even as the shouting goes on, it begins to lose conviction, wearying of its own falsehood. Such is the magic of the Buddha's power of compassion. Now the shouting stops totally, in the way in which the cries of birds and beasts stop suddenly when a tiger is sighted in a forest, and we are blessed with a vision of the Tathāgata's poise of being. Unraised, deep as a roaring river yet gentle as a mountain-stream, the Tathāgata's voice is heard. The words uttered — and recorded in the 'Bhaddavaggiyavatthu' text with the ordinariness of the ring of truth—are a compassionately confounding counter-question: "Which would be better for you; that you should go in search of a woman, or that you should go in search of self?"

What magic is this! Such unbelievable resolution of anger and doubt and vindictiveness! The aristocratic faces are confused by compassion, shamed into lack-lusterness by the limitless light and beauty of the face of truth. The authority of that voice of compassion, the sound of Dharma itself, scatters the hunters and s, runs; falling down, getting up, running and falling ng again.

rch party destroys the tranquillity of the forest, dis- ecology of the "araṇya," literally "that which cannot be a metaphor of self, a promise and a place of peace. The valking up and down in one corner of the forest; the flight in the deep recesses of the forest; and the en- tructive aristocrats determined to hunt her down and riously driven by destiny closer and closer to where the self is. Work for cameras in helicopters and hope for the tened.

n loses sight of the hunted woman now, but discovers ha in moonlit, ethereal, close-ups. Not quite the face at only the hem of the kaṣāya, saffron robe, the blessed d in jñāna mudrā, gesture of gnosis; and then the sāṃ- rldly, roar of the search party as it invades the territory thāgata. Haughty men and women discourteously ac- he Lord. We only see the back of his head, *gheraoing*[22] are these representatives of high birth. In a chorus of ey ask the Buddha if the ungrateful wretch has passed if he has heard her cries; if he has any information at all g her which can help them catch and punish her suita- h-bearers close in, and the whole effrontery is made ible.

en as the shouting goes on, it begins to lose conviction, of its own falsehood. Such is the magic of the Buddha's compassion. Now the shouting stops totally, in the way the cries of birds and beasts stop suddenly when a tiger d in a forest, and we are blessed with a vision of the Tath- oise of being. Unraised, deep as a roaring river yet gentle ntain-stream, the Tathāgata's voice is heard. The words — and recorded in the 'Bhaddavaggiyavatthu' text with ariness of the ring of truth—are a compassionately con- counter-question: "Which would be better for you; that uld go in search of a woman, or that you should go in f self?"

magic is this! Such unbelievable resolution of anger and d vindictiveness! The aristocratic faces are confused by sion, shamed into lack-lusterness by the limitless light ty of the face of truth. The authority of that voice of com- , the sound of Dharma itself, scatters the hunters and

The aim of the symposium is to debate the issues arising out of the Buddha's advice to aristocracy to seek self and not revenge against an escaped and thieving slave: an ādivāsī girl called Ananyā who has taken refuge in the Buddha, and who claims she stole the valuables of her masters to make an offering of them to Sītā at her kitchen shrine in Ayodhyā as a gesture of atonement for humanity's violation of the integrity of consciousness and the ecology of nature.

What is at stake is the honor of Indian spiritual traditions[20] and the fate of life and civilization on earth. What is offered is a testimony of faith and inquiry.

SĪTĀ'S KITCHE

I

The Buddha is in a forest near Vārāṇasī,
a clearing in the forest, savoring the peac
over craving that he has won. A scene for
the earth and all her creatures from the
Precisely at that point in time, somewhere
a group of revelers are lost in their pleas
tocracy, the beautiful people of the great ci
Vārāṇasī, Śrāvastī, etc. The only person i
not have a partner is a slave girl whose re
after the valuables of the lovers lost in the

Think of the powerful beautiful instru
dha's solitary, leonine, immersion in the l
bondage of the couples to fleeting pleas
nessed perhaps by the self-same full mo
capture this mysterious similarity and d
vāṇa and saṃsāra in a film version of the
'Bhaddavaggiyavatthu'[21] (translatable as
which tells this story?

The slave woman runs away with the v
naments — of her owners. Surely the self
To leave anyone out of the sphere of love an
wrath of retribution. The lovers awaken f
dulgence, and finding their valuables gon
custodian, they are furious beyond meas
great film. Beautiful selfish men and wo
ugly wrath on their faces, self-righteous
think their trust has been betrayed by a m
for the thief is launched. No doubt not onl
back too. Perhaps elephants too are press
rified face of the girl caught intermittent

runs, r
and ru
The s
turbs th
battled
Buddh
woman
raged
yet mys
Lord hi
unenlig
The
the Bu
once, b
feet, h
sāric,
of the
costing
him so
voices
that w
regard
bly. To
sadly
But
weary
power
in whic
is sigh
āgata's
as a m
uttere
the ord
foundi
you sh
search
Wha
doubt
compa
and be
passio

shatters their pride for a while at least, although some among them in the background remain unconvinced though not unimpressed. Too bad for doctrinaire Buddhism and Hinduism, this is a complete upaniṣad!

Although the text does not say so, news of the humiliation and illumination of the lords and ladies in the forest would have spread, causing a great debate to arise amongst the intelligentsia of the age. Ātmabodha, self-knowledge, would have dawned again here and there in that self-forgetful age dominated by the nihilism of the likes of Ajita Keśakambalin and Makkhali Gośāla, known contemporaries of the Buddha and Mahāvīra. The missing slave girl is a powerful symbol both of the true extra dimension of existence, Ātman, self, which we must seek and not the fulfilment of extra desires; and of the power of desire to run away with our peace of mind. There is no record of the Buddha and Mahāvīra meeting Ajita Keśakambalin and Makkhali Gośāla in metaphysical and moral debate. Let us imagine such a meeting: an ancestral altercation between nirvāna and nihilism, ahimsā and absurdism, advaita and annihilationism. Let us imagine a great forest symposium precipitated by the 'Bhaddavaggiyavatthu' encounter of self-forgetfulness and self-realization.

II

We can plausibly suppose that the nihilist philosophers Ajita and Makkhali would have been in close contact with thinking and self-doubting members of the aristocracy of their times. Fictionally, let us also suppose that they knew quite well several members of the forest party of the 'Bhaddavaggiyavatthu' story; and not only the likes of the slave girl of that story, but the self-same betrayer of trust was also not unknown to them.

We can imagine some of the forest group seeking out Ajita and Makkhali and reporting to them their mysterious meeting in the forest with the Tathāgata which opened their eyes to the pointlessness of their pleasure-seeking exploitativeness and the neglect of the truth of self and the tradition of self-inquiry which fueled their greed; but out of deference to the prestige of the nihilist masters, they would have couched their report in a suitable language of understatement and agnosticism. Perhaps some of these kṣatriyas would also have angrily confronted complacent court Brāhmaṇas, accusing them of being unworthy trustees and transmitters of the upaniṣadic heritage of self-inquiry. Many others would have been genuinely perplexed and troubled by the forest episode.

Exploring possibilities further, it is quite likely that the slave girl was aware of the Buddha's presence in the forest and found her way to him after the embarrassed exit of her pursuers from the scene. He knew it all, she wouldn't have had to say anything. Perhaps he would have commended to her the trusteeship of self as being far worthier than trading in flesh, but no doubt with the utmost compassion and concern for the inequitous circumstances of her life. The Buddha would have represented to her something noble which is not the right of birth but the light of realization, and to which she too was heir. The nobility of freedom from ignorance and craving and suffering.

Ajita and Makkhali too would have run into the liberated slave in the market place and heard her version of the mysterious forest happenings, which would have more than confirmed — to their discomfiture — what the intellectual aristocrats would have told them. The cynical wizards would have heaped scorn on the alleged transformation of the noblemen and their ladies and tried to shake the young woman's new found faith in the possibility of overcoming covetousness and the pull of the flesh, faith in nirvāṇa and kaivalya and mokṣa, Buddha and Mahāvīra and Ātman. And they would have summoned a seminar, a great forest debate, in defense of their unexpectedly challenged intellectual authority.

Perhaps the slave girl's name was 'Ananyā,' which means "No Other,"; i.e. Ātman, oneself, which is what the Buddha had asked her pursuers to seek: singular self imaged in all beings, the true surplus of existence of which the excesses of our covetousness are such a costly caricature. We can imagine Ajita and Makkhali in a gesture of defiance, and as indicative of their championship of the cause of the oppressed, asking Ananyā personally to convey to the Buddha their desire to engage him publicly in a debate on the meaning of life. And they would have conveyed a similar challenge to Mahāvīra through their contacts in the Tīrthaṃkara's camp. And of course those who started it all, the gullible aristocrats, and Brāhmaṇical philosophers, and sundry other categories of people, would also have been called.

Contemptuously, Ajita and Makkhali would probably have chosen as the venue for the debate they were demanding the ample shade of the banyan tree under which first her tormentors, and later Ananyā herself, had encountered the Buddha. Rooted in the ground, a vast cluster of the great banyan's branches would have fashioned around the tree's central trunk a seminar space resembling a many-pillared hall of traditional scholarly debate. Such is the intellectual prestige of the nihilist duo, and so great is the importance of their challenge, that they receive no "regrets" messages from any of the invitees.

Ajita Keśakambalin would not have occupied the central position under the tree against the main trunk. Not out of humility, true or false, but to make the point that he did not believe that there was any centre to anything at all; to drive home the deeper aspect of his eccentricity, i.e. off-centeredness. He would have sat leaning against one of the rooted branches of the great tree, but not in padmāsana — the lotus sitting posture — which again presupposes poise of being. He would have sat with one leg fully stretched out and pointing in the direction of the Buddha seated comfortably but respectfully in sukhāsana — unstrained sitting posture — on the periphery of the Seminar Circle, the other leg arched at the knee: thus showing not so much his disrespect for authority as his unbelief in it. His blanket of hair — for that is what he wore, as the name Keśakambalin suggests, like John the Baptist — would have glistened in the late afternoon sun, proclaiming his ascetic eminence; and the strength of his followers and admirers crowding animatedly behind and alongside him and forming a wide arc of support would have established his unquestionable chairmanship of the occasion.

Swinging upside down from a more conventional horizontal branch of the banyan, and quite close to Ajita, would be Makkhali Gośāla: Vice-chairman and philosophical acrobat given to the habit of dangling from branches of trees in the bat-position so as to underscore the upside-downness, topsy-turvyness, of being and becoming, the indignity and irrationality of reality.

Face-to-face with this arc of denial and doubt would be another arc along which directly opposite Ajita's outstretched leg but quite untroubled by it, is the Buddha with a sprinkling of bhikṣus and others on either side of him. And at a slight distance from the Tathāgata—a distance of respect and variety, not of disrespect or duality — is Mahāvīra, seated in the strictest padmāsana, gently flanked by a small number of brahmacārīs and munis of his order. Buddha and Mahāvīra recognize each other wordlessly in the way of jñānīs, and one suspects that they have not brought along with them anything like a crowd of their followers so as not to present an image separately, and together, of anxious and defensive solidarity in the face of nihilist defiance.

The arc is completed on either side of the Buddha and Mahāvīra by members of the kṣatriya aristocracy amongst whom can be recognized several of those, men and women, who had encountered the Buddha in the forest; and by representatives of Brāhmaṇical orthodoxy (members of both categories of high birth and authority can be seen dotting the arc of Ajita's camp also).

On one side of this fairly large circle, and several diffident feet behind where the two arcs meet, is a huddle of tribal people — ādivāsīs — and śūdras, amongst whom and at their head with eyes flashing nervously from Buddha and Mahāvīra to Ajita and Makkhali and back, is Ananyā, on her knees, awe-struck and yet with a fresh radiance of realization and a sense of the intervention of destiny not only in her life but in the process of life itself.

All humanity in all aspects seems to be represented in the circle under the tree. Sage and cynic, high and low born, men and women, master and slave, ādivāsī and avant-garde, orthodox and rebellious, defiant and repentant, all find representation. But isn't nature excluded — matter and non-human life? And isn't nothingness or emptiness also excluded from Ajita's anthropocentric colloquium, that which is not a thing of any kind at all? Excluded from concern and as reality?

One can imagine nature registering the fear that such exclusion might be a fact, despite the presence in the closed circle of a Buddha and a Mahāvīra. A sun in flight casting beautiful but ominous shadows on the ground, striping and tattooing self-centered humanity with elusive jungle reflections, indignant signatures of what is excluded. The arrival and sudden apparently unprovoked flight of deer; the unnaturally contrite and sullen cawing and sniggering of crows and sparrows; the unworthily strident and frightened trumpeting and roaring of a distant elephant and tiger; and such other signs of disorientation and dread and appeals for inclusion and protests against exclusion.

These signs do not escape the attention of ascetic Ajita and alert Makkhali. However, they read them as affirmations of absurdity, not as evidence of exclusion. Then amazingly (but not really amazingly, for a steady current of compassion has radiated from the Buddha and Mahāvīra towards all creatures of the forest, all structures of existence, and merged with the emptiness between and within and beyond all things) these signs die down and are replaced by more self-confident bird song, more self-respecting roaring and trumpeting of tiger and elephant; and the deer reappear. And the sun floods the circle with a slanting but steady and large cone of light, and is no longer in flight.

This apparent reversal of audio-visual support for absurdism upsets Makkhali, who does a couple of swings on his branch and lands with a thud and a big false smile on the ground near Ajita, causing Ajita to inaugurate the forest inquiry at once.

III

Thus spoke Ajita Keśakambalin:

> Gotama (the Buddha) and Vardhamāna (Mahāvīra), Brāhmaṇas and kṣatriyas, priests and paurāṇikas, merchants and patrons of the arts, artists and ascetics, freethinking philosophers and sectarian dogmatists, āryans and ādivāsīs, high and low born, men and women, friends and enemies, fellow nihilists and sentimental survivalists: listen!
>
> It has been reported to us — to Makkhali and myself — by some young men and women of noble birth who are our friends, and who have been our followers, that recently they along with several of their companions encountered Gotama in this forest, indeed under this very tree where we are assembled, and that he persuaded them not to hunt down an escaped slave but to seek, instead, the self! The impressionable young inheritors of kingdoms have also been cultivating the company of Vardhamāna who has almost persuaded them that not only is it wrong to hunt down escaped slaves, but that it is no less wrong to hunt any creatures at all, to harm or destroy any form of life deliberately and avoidably!
>
> As a result of these encounters with illumination and harmlessness, these upstart revolutionaries have taken to harassing Brāhmaṇa scholars, accusing them of conjuring up irresolvable metaphysical differences between the traditions of the Veda and Vedānta and the teachings of Gotama and Vardhamāna in order to conceal the common socially, morally, and eco-

logically revolutionary consequences of the truth of these traditions and teachings.

My own and Makkhali's uncompromisingly negative views regarding metaphysics and religion, Vedic or Vedāntic or contemporary, and especially regarding the possibility and desirability of reconciling conflicting metaphysical and religious traditions and positions, are very well and widely known; and in any case we haven't convened this colloquium to discuss tiresome and trivial metaphysical matters or to reject or resurrect religion in any form. We have a prophecy to make, and we want to make it in the presence of representative humanity such as this assembly, and to arrest the dangerous optimism recently generated in the young (who ought to know better) by Gotama and Vardhamāna before it overwhelms this land and eventually also other lands beyond the mountains and the seas. Unburden yourselves of thought and theory, then, of revelation and revolution and realization, and hear our prophecy.

Makkhali could hardly contain his excitement and swung back to his branch and his inverted bat-position and swayed backwards and forwards ominously for an interminable minute suggestive of a countdown for catastrophe, somersaulted, and was deposited back on his patch of vice-chairmanship next to Ajita. Ananyā trembled and linked arms with girl-friends on either side of her in an instinctive and desperate gesture of togetherness.

Ajita continued:

We prophesy that humanity, indeed the earth as a whole, will confront an unprecedented crisis of survival and self-confidence two and a half to three thousand years from now. The world then, as it is now, will be deeply divided socio-economically, ideologically, territorially, racially, and theologically and metaphysically; the only difference being that the depth of these divisions then will be as staggering as will be the size of the human population. Violence, the standard and perfectly understandable human response to conflict, will have failed to generate enduring victories for nations and other collectivities and ideologies over one another; but its willing allies, science and technology, would bring into existence weapons of destruction capable of annihilating not only human life but all life on earth several times over.

As Ajita uttered these last ominous words, he became aware of the shrill buzzing of a halo of mosquitoes behind and around his head, and a sudden significant drop in temperature despite the steadiness of sunlight under the tree. Taking these signs as confirmatory of his predictions, Ajita looked self-congratulatorily first at the Buddha, then at Mahāvīra, and turned his face in the direction of Makkhali in a gesture of most encouraging affection, darted a "you ought to have known better" look at Ananyā, and continued as follows:

> Most contending collectivities will come to possess these weapons of destruction and a common fear of mutual and total destruction will force them uneasily to coexist in peace for a while. But secretly, the search for new weapons of destruction and modes of immobilizing the destructive potential of enemies will not of course be irrationally abandoned; and the permanent possibility of accidents or impulsiveness starting a chain of uncontrollable explosions of destruction will bring to the condition of absence of war a dimension of dread no more comfortable than the horrors of actual war.
>
> To be sure, novel, non-violent, organized and insistent attempts will also be made by optimistic groups of lovers of life to resolve conflicts and reduce tensions and curtail armaments, inspired at heart by the sort of foolish example recently set by Gotama right here in this forest which has necessitated this assembly; and by the kind of unworkable and self-deceiving romanticism implicit in Vardhamāna's preaching of reverence for all life. But non-violence will not melt hearts nor deflect human collectivities from their violent designs upon one another, although admittedly there will come to be attached to some leaders of non-violent movements the sort of dubious spiritual and moral prestige that now attaches to the likes of Gotama and Vardhamāna.

Resenting this pointed insult to goodness and greatness, several followers and admirers of the Buddha and Mahāvīra got up to leave the assembly at this point and others too lowered their heads in embarrassment, but the protesters sat down again as the two jñānīs raised their right hands in abhaya mudrā, the gesture of peace and offer of the blessing of fearlessness to all beings. The double boon, like some lens correction, suddenly brought all the colours of the forest more sharply into focus, even as the light under and around the banyan assumed a more rarefied but golden dimension.

Disappointed at this non-violent outcome of provocation, Makkhali pretended to yawn and Ajita summoned a false, toothy, "all right, I apologize" expression on his face and resumed his prophesying.

> Even more conducive to the collapse of self-confidence and civilization than the failure of the missions of violence and non-violence will be the ecologically depredatory life-style which the vast majority of human beings and societies, rich and poor alike, will come increasingly to adopt. This life-style will eventually drain the earth's very finite resources of nourishment to a dangerously low level, lowering to the same level the quality of human life and humanity's will to live.
>
> For the first time in history, large human populations will conceive of collective suicide inarticulately but irresistibly. Philosophers and even theologians, who will be our followers in that age, will fearlessly spell out the implications of this conception. They will utter the unutterable thought: that annihilation is not a curse but a blessing. Gotama and Vardhamāna and Brāhmaṇa scholars, your followers too will be around then; they will first be laughed at, and then despised for having deluded humanity into optimism for so long; and then they will be offered to the Nihil as the first sacrifice of a consciously and gladly collectively self-destructive human species!

Bewildering even to his followers and admirers who, while feeling elated that their leader was making a series of apparently telling and winning points against his adversaries, also simultaneously felt strangely robbed by him of their humanity, and sickening as he seemed to others (although the Buddha and Mahāvīra did not waver at all in their concentrated listening), Ajita found from this point onwards that he was simply allowed to go on and on by the assembly; and go on and on he did, as follows:

> Don't let anyone get away with the thought that this consummation of history will be achieved through timid euthanasia! It will be the crowning culmination of the majority of the human species continuing, perhaps accelerating, all their ecologically and mutually hostile activities. It will be in the midst of a glorious, but all too short, period of morally and spiritually unhampered indulgence of ego in enjoyment and aggression that the explosions of the final solution and the collapse of life-systems will occur. The dying will not envy any likely survivors, for there will be none; and they will suddenly see in this un-

availability of envy the unexpected moral rectitude of their unique act!

All other life too will be ended by the holocaust. I know this will sound like monstrous avoidable cruelty to some of you; I know some of you will think the frightened thought that in so far as the human species is permitted collective suicide, it can only be permitted selective suicide, and by no means at all can it be entitled to murder all other species of life. What childish nonsense! It is non-human life's frenzy of mutual devouring, perfectly amoral and relentless, suggestive of life's hankering after death, being's hunger for nothingness, which is at the foundation of the human experiment in peace and civilization, religion and spiritual realization. Isn't it thus only appropriate that in the ultimate holocaust which future humanity will unleash, the foundation should perish along with the superstructure? Ha ha ha ha ha ha!

Makkhali whistled continuously in delight as accompaniment to the nihilist music of Ajita's lurid laughter, and the duo brought their fists punitively down on the ground a terrible number of times.

The earth, which had not too long before this event borne witness to the reality of the Buddha's enlightenment at the insistence of Māra, the tempter, who had mocked at the Tathāgata's claim to it, now trembled in witness of the Keśakambalin's threat to it. Tremors set off a forest cacophony of anxiety and the assembly sat glued to the ground in panic. Ananyā, and perhaps only she, noticed that the Buddha's eyes were closed in deeply-indrawn meditation and his palms, downward-facing but not touching the ground, offered abhaya, fearlessness, to the earth. The tremors ceased quietly and quickly enough, Ajita taking this geological interlude to be the deepest demonstration of the truth —and power—of his prophesying.

Moving in for the kill now, as he thought, Ajita started rapidly to sum up his challenge; giving chase, so it seemed, to the retreating sun.

Vardhamāna! he thundered. Those tremors were not an earthquake but a footnote to what I was saying about life's inevitably annihilationist destiny, a reminder that material reality too in its hidden depths is a cauldron of ferocious causal interaction between its imperceptible constituents (it is this seed material energy of violence which will fuel the all-destructive weaponry of the future). All your talk of ahiṃsā or non-violence is a wishful falsification of the violence or hiṃsā with which all existence throbs, a pitiable piece of self-deception which will stand fully exposed in that future time of holocaust and honesty that I have been talking about. Do you not see that with every breath of righteous indignation that Ananyā breathes and with every breath that you and Gotama waste in meditation, millions of microbes are consigned to nothingness? Consistency requires that you and all your followers should fast unto death in protest against the violence at the heart of existence. Why don't you do so?

And all your talk of nirvāṇa and emptiness, Gotama, is but a pathetic sublimation of nothingness which so utterly exceeds, invades, surrounds, and swallows up paltry existence, even as the trampling march of human history will reduce to a desert this proud forest. And please don't imagine, Gotama, that by reminding the Brāhmaṇical tradition of the identity between upaniṣadic self-realization and nirvāṇic enlightenment, between Ātman and Śūnyatā, self and emptiness, you advance the cause of truth. For upaniṣadic self-realization is the grandest of delusions, as I thought you were well set to discover in your search for enlightenment. But you chickened out when you dressed up nothingness as nirvāṇa; for thus dressed up, nothingness does indeed also look like mokṣa.

But I prophesy that your followers and future Brāhmaṇical philosophers will not even see this. With welcome, but wasteful, sectarian violence, and marvelous but misguided sophistication, they will succeed in convincing themselves and others that mokṣa and nirvāṇa, self and emptiness, have nothing to do with each other. They will not see that both are masks put on the terrifying face of nothingness; i.e., not until annihilation becomes a temptation. It is not the middle, Gotama, that in their deepest thrust all things seek, but the end, if you will pardon a pun.

The sun had disappeared, but the western sky was dramatically illumined still and awash with futurist brush strokes of red and blue and gold and formed a fiendishly beautiful backdrop to the colloquium under the palatial tree.

After a brief interlude during which disciples massaged Ajita's rheumatic legs, Makkhali climbed higher and deeper into the recesses of the banyan scaffolding, others gathered in small groups and whispered gravely, the Buddha and Mahāvīra exchanged glances of compassionate resignation and fed nuts to squirrels and deer, Ananyā sought softly but animatedly to explain the gist of Ajita's disquisition to her friends, and when everyone — including Makkhali who came violently sliding down from the treetop — had returned to their seats on the ground, Ajita spoke slowly again thus:

> Brāhmaṇa priests, scholars, philosophers, listen to me. If Makkhali and I had been moral romanticists, we would have railed against the wickedly inequitous Brāhmaṇical social code which keeps the likes of Ananyā permanently in subjugation, and we would have commended to you the apparently more egalitarian social outlook of Gotama and Vardhamāna.
>
> But we are not moral romanticists, we believe that all social systems are untruthful, because in their essential cocooning function — and even the most inegalitarian society performs this function — they present to their constituents a false benign microcosmic picture of the universe which is in reality the steady devouring march of nothingness against all existence, human or non-human, individual or collective. The corruptibility of even revolutionary, egalitarian, social systems is to be traced to this root untruthfulness. Indeed we predict that in the centuries ahead, the orders established by Gotama and Vardhamāna will decline in moral authority and will not succeed in rejuvenating or supplanting Brāhmaṇical social orthodoxy which has been in moral decline for several centuries now.
>
> A false sense of an ultimate social and metaphysical incompatibility between Brāhmaṇism and Buddhism, especially, and between these and other forms of thought and life — which will arrive in this land along with conquerors from distant parts of the world — will cause sufficient strife here to enable the best minds and hearts of Bhāratavarṣa in two or three millennia to join the best of the rest of the world in proposing, in the then obtaining ecologically devastated and militarily explosive and psychologically traumatized conditions of life, the final solution to the problem of life: global death. The epics say it all. Rāma's abandonment of Sītā in the Rāmāyaṇa is the letting down of life by truth itself; and despite Kṛṣṇa's active involvement in the Mahābhārata events, self-destructiveness is unstoppable. What more is there to say to you? Embrace the secret annihilationism of your tradition!
>
> Poor dear Ananyā, I understand that through the mediation of Gotama, and in exchange for your freedom, you have returned to your erstwhile masters and mistresses the jewelry

that you took from them. No loss, really. Those ornaments represent the foolish optimism of the deluded classes of the world, ruling or ruled over: optimism regarding the chances of petty existence surrounded on all sides and penetrated by nothingness. You used to wear a wonderful cynical smile on your face which you have lost since your recent meeting with Gotama; your true ornament it was. I want to give you back that piece of jewelry, your cynical smile. A thousand Gotamas and Vardhamānas can't take it away from you, your right to be rid of the enslaving optimism called life and civilization and spiritual realization. Come back to us again, Ananyā, and these lords and ladies will follow you this time not as hunters but as slaves: all of us ancestors of annihilation!

As he uttered these last words of his oration, Ajita seemed overcome with emotion, an impression he quickly sought to correct by manifesting a fit of coughing. Makkhali thumped his back vigorously, mainly congratulatorily and partly, of course, to ease the coughing. Ananyā covered her face with her hands and sobbed uncontrollably. Two young ladies hurried to where Ananyā was and knelt on either side of her and comforted her, deserting their privileged seats amongst the aristocrats by the side of Ajita. They had belonged to the 'Bhaddavaggiya' group of Ananyā's tormentors.

IV

Night had been coming on, and three torches were lit even as Ajita was speaking and held aloft by tall servants of noblemen standing behind Ajita and Makkhali. Flickering in the mild evening breeze, the flames projected intricately mobile and changeful patterns on the ground between the two arcs of the assembly, which could be seen — and were seen — as representing either chaos or vibrant interdependence at the heart of reality, depending on how far from despair or close to it you were in that age of nihilism and nirvāṇa.

Several minutes passed without anyone speaking. The flickering, sputtering, torch flares and their ambiguous shadow play, tired coughing, widening alarmist cricket sounds, and above all, the numbing of conscience and consciousness which had been brought on by Ajita's speech, had generated a most tangible atmosphere of defeat under the banyan which neither the stars in the sky nor the moonlit clouds above a whole horizon of trees behind the Buddha and Mahāvīra did anything to alleviate. (It was a night of the full moon but the luminary had not been sighted yet.)

Makkhali, who had been standing on his head for a long time, suddenly somersaulted back to the sitting-down position with a squeal of delight, and was about to raise Ajita's right arm to signal a walk-over victory for nihilism, when his and everyone's attention was hijacked by a perfectly round moon which rose abruptly above the trees and the clouds behind the Buddha and Mahāvīra and stood directly between the two jñānīs. The Buddha and Mahāvīra alone did not turn around to look at the nightwatchman, for he merely represented their own function in that dark age of doubt and despair when the sun of self-realization had seemed to have set forever. The light of the full moon flooded the assembly with cooling compassion and all faces became quite visible, making it unnecessary to light more torches; but some were lit nevertheless and torchbearers dotted the whole circle now.

His form exquisitely silhouetted by moonlight, the Buddha raised his right hand in abhaya mudrā, and spoke thus:

> Ajita, may you be at peace with yourself. Acute thinker that you are, you have nevertheless allowed unfairness to enter into your thought and vitiate your judgement. You have been unfair toward a fellow human being, Mahāvīra; also toward non-human life, toward material reality, and toward nothingness.
>
> You have attributed to Mahāvīra a view which is not his, namely, that non-human life is an arena of unrestrained violence and slaughter of life by life. As far as I know, Mahāvīra acknowledges that by and large non-human life exemplifies admirable and adequate ecological restraint: non-human living beings rarely kill beyond the needs and necessities of survival, and although their struggle for survival is relentless and violent, their lives also poignantly exhibit the non-violent dimensions of playfulness and love and nurturing. It is also worth bearing in mind that while the ecological discipline exemplified by non-human life is probably largely instinctual, this fact only highlights the 'naturalness' of such discipline and does not undermine its reality or wisdom.

> Mahāvīra is at pains to point out that it is singularly the human species which massively and dangerously violates life's deeply embedded code of ecological honor, wildly beyond the claims of need and necessity being the scale of its slaughter of non-human life. And this propensity of the human species to ecological evil is rooted in the ignorance and unwisdom of its modes of living, in individual and collective ego; and not in some basic flaw in the nature and process of life as such, as you imagine. So you have been unfair to Mahāvīra and to the status of non-human life. And. . . .

But the Buddha was interrupted here by Makkhali, who, stung by the charge of unfairness leveled at Ajita by the Tathāgata, leapt back to his swinging branch and hissed and hooted as he swayed back and forth, to the great annoyance of the vast majority of seminarists — including several Ajita loyalists — who had been listening to the Buddha with rapt attention. There was whispered indignation, but no real protest.

While the Buddha had been speaking, Ajita had rudely turned his frame entirely towards his admirers; and with shrugged shoulders and an expression of exasperation on his face, sought wordlessly to belittle the words of the Buddha. But the force of the Tathāgata's testimony was undeniable, and confidence was quickly turning into nervous anger in Ajita's heart. Taking advantage of the interruption secured by Makkhali's acrobatics, Ajita violently swung round and was face-to-face with the Buddha once again, and reprimanded him as follows:

> Stop this nitpicking, Gotama. What difference does it make if human destructiveness is rooted in the flawed character of life itself or in ego? Ego is ineradicable, so the doom I prophesy is also unavoidable. If you will pardon my saying so, Gotama and Vardhamāna, contemporary new-fangled spirituality such as yours is without the epic worldly wisdom of the Brāhmaṇical tradition; although I am afraid under your influence Brāhmaṇa scholars of our time are likely gravely to misconceive their own traditions. In the Rāmāyaṇa and the Mahābhārata, as I had pointed out earlier, the supposedly divine Rāma and Kṛṣṇa are themselves not without ego and consequently become vehicles of injustice and destruction. Rāma abandons his faithful wife Sītā to placate his rebellious subjects, such is the lure of power; and such indeed is ego's secret hatred of life itself, for Sītā represents the energy of life. And Kṛṣṇa engineers the total de-

struction of the Kauravas because of his special love for the Pāṇdavas, such is the violent selectivity of egoistic love.

Where incarnations have failed to uphold civilization, how can so-called sages like yourselves or your successors save life on earth? Ego and its counterpart, recalcitrant and explosive material reality, will draw all life into the net of nothingness. The future will bear me out, I promise you.

Subtly, Ajita thus tried to flatter Brāhmaṇa members of the assembly into distrusting the Buddha and Mahāvīra; and as soon as he had delivered himself of the above diatribe, he turned his gaze eagerly in the direction of a group of Brāhmaṇas seated roughly half-way between himself and the Buddha, almost opposite Ananyā on the other side of the assembly circle, longing for words of approbation from them, even a nod of assent. But the Brāhmaṇas were quite embarrassed and upset too and did not acknowledge Ajita's gaze, and looked instead in the direction of the Buddha, wanting to give him the benefit of a response; for the Tathāgata had been interrupted and insulted.

Makkhali dropped back to his seat and cupped his ears with his hands, indicating that he did not want to listen to the Buddha; and then stood on his head with his posterior turned towards the Tathāgata. Clouds hid the moon in shame for a while, then drifted off proudly as the Buddha began to speak again, quite unmindful of Makkhali's insult; and more compassionately than ever.

Mahāvīra and I may have annoyed you, Ajita, because of the sharpness of the opposition between our teachings and yours; but what have material reality and nothingness done to incur your wrath? Material reality is certainly vast and turbulent, even as it is dense and impenetrable and infinitesimal. But it is the datelessly long experience of all creatures of the earth and the sky and the oceans that even the most cataclysmic winds and fires and floods and quakings of land pass; life is not overrun by the fury of the elements, nor of course do they indulge it sentimentally.

The causality of materiality, large or medium or small scale, is suffused with self-restraint. Our experience of duration, of the lived present moment, is without doubt a pure gift of causality's self-restraint: materiality's choice of a middle ground between overwhelming efficaciousness and unstimulating, unproductive, inertia.

Limitless explosive energy is indeed locked away in the recesses of matter, harmlessly for life's sake, even as Śiva in sacred mythology keeps locked away in his throat the poison which emerged along with nectar during the churning of the ocean of possibilities at the time of creation; and which asuras long to possess as an ultimate resource of destructiveness. Śiva's throat is blue because annihilatory poison is safely stored away there, a truth nobly mirrored by the accommodating blue of sky and sea.

It is not impossible that future humanity will fall into the āsuric temptation of breaking open the secret vaults of matter and robbing it of untameable energy in the service of greed and terror and endanger all life on earth, as you rightly point out, Ajita. But don't be unfair again, do not make human folly unredeemable by grounding it this time in some alleged unrestrained causal fury at the heart of the nature of material process and reality. Causality everywhere is compassionate in its reined-in effectuality. It is not hiṃsā, but ahiṃsā, which is rooted in the nature of life and matter; and nothingness, which too, Ajita, you malign.

Instead of the violent interruption that one would have expected at this point from Ajita and Makkhali, a perplexing calm began to enter even their hardened hearts; and inexplicably, Makkhali found himself abandoning his posterior headstand and assuming an alert sitting down position, although he kept looking at Ajita's face nervously from time to time, and Ajita at his, as the Buddha proceeded with his disquisition:

Self-restraint or self-limitation is even more dramatically exemplified by nothingness than by life or material reality. Look at the vastness of space within which are manifest all worlds everywhere, including our sun and moon and earth and this blessed forest and all of us inquirers assembled here. That any manifestation at all is permitted within it by the limitless vastness of space is a miracle of self-restraint, the austerest ecological discipline conceivable, the purest ahiṃsā.

Nothingness is not a *thing* in competition with other things. Indeed it is continuous with the heart of each thing which is also a not-thingness, like the selfhood of human personality which is also not a being in competition with other beings and things but the limitless space of not-thingness, emptiness. The practice of compassion by human beings is a realization of the omnipresence of self or nothingness, and also a realization thus of their identity: the identity of self-realization and nirvāṇa which are not, Ajita, masks put on the terrifying face of nothingness, because nothingness, although no unreality, is no thing and not at all terrifying, being the heart of all things and ourselves. Only when we misconstrue nothingness as a limitless *something*, and misconstrue ourselves as limited *things*, does nothingness appear to us as a devouring, annihilatory, malevolence, and human consciousness congeals in fear in relation to its own monstrous misconception, hardening its heart toward life and the possibilities of civilization and realization and invites apocalypse.

Do not declare war against reality, Ajita, because reality doesn't declare war against anything. The nihilism you preach and the self-centeredness you pardon are caricatures of the pacifying compassion of nothingness and the joyous explosiveness of self-realization. But even caricature points to reality, deceivingly but dramatically, and cynicism and doomsaying are great awakeners of conscience and consciousness and life from sleep and dream and complacency: so we are grateful to you, Ajita. May peace be with you.

Everyone was deeply touched—and even Ajita and Makkhali were troubled—by that benediction with which the Buddha concluded his last contribution to the colloquium, and the assembly felt greatly reassured by his words about the nature of things and nothingness and selfhood and life; but not everyone was reassured about the future of life and civilization on earth. For the very perversion of logic and inversion of priorities and subversion of confidence which had characterized Ajita's rhetoric reminded many in the assembly of humanity's deep vulnerability precisely to these deviations from truth; and fear lurked in many a heart of an apocalyptic retribution for cumulative human sinning which could not be neutralized by the illumination of a Mahāvīra or a Buddha or by the tradition of the sages of antiquity. And if Ajita was right about Rāma's denial and Kṛṣṇa's destructiveness, what could even future avatāras do to avert annihilation?

But was Ajita right about Rāma and Kṛṣṇa? Are the Rāmāyaṇa and Mahābhārata nihilist tragedies?

The Brāhmaṇa scholars whose approbation Ajita had wordlessly but humiliatingly sought for his weird reading of the sacred epics were shattered by the experience and had fallen into prayerful meditation. Also convulsed with anxiety by Ajita's sacrilege were the two young aristocratic ladies who had rushed to Ananyā's aid when she had been reduced to traumatic sobbing by the salacious cynic's perverted praise of her.

V

Very irregularly shaped and dense clouds suddenly concealed the moon and a whole train of them went on doing so, permitting only fractional intermittent glimpses of it, rather like a stretch of Ajita's petulant interruptions of the Buddha. This new scheme of the sky gave the Keśakambalin a dream of an opportunity to try and undo the magic which had been wrought over the assembly by the Tathāgata's discourse.

Laughing luridly once again, and to the accompaniment of Makkhali's continuous clapping, Ajita sprang to his feet, and with both arms raised and clenched fists, thundered forth the following prophecy:

> Say what you will, Gotama, and stay as silent as you wish, Vardhamāna, but I prophesy once again that in less than three millennia from now, the illumination of your speech and silence will only be laughably and trivially visible beneath an unstoppable procession of annihilationist aspirations even as that fat moon is behind those gloriously defiant clouds. Say what you will, all of you, sentimentalists hallucinated by hope and drugged by light!

The dramatic power of these words was chilling, but the voice also betrayed the tiredness of bravado and the surfacing stammer of deeply repressed guilt, quickly repressed again though this was. Mock-heroically, and as though struck down by punitive lightning for speaking bitter truth, Ajita fell to the ground in an ascetic heap, but was quickly enough revived and straightened out by Makkhali's false but loud lamentations and comradely massage.

Amazingly, Ajita's revival exactly coincided with the liberation of the moon from the censorship of the clouds whose procession ended as abruptly as it had begun. Light and darkness, hope and despair, seemed once again not unequal to one another in the universe and under the witnessing tree, whose silent non-violent power was matched and reinforced by Mahāvīra sitting as straight and still as the banyan's main trunk and who did not yield to the temptation of speech throughout the proceedings of the assembly. Nor, to be fair, did Makkhali, who confined himself to non-verbal noise-making and acrobatic activity and service to Ajita, although only the last piece of behavior could safely be described as non-violent.

Equally amazingly, precisely at this climatically and philosophically favorable moment, as though assisted by some astrobiological mechanism, one of the tormented Brāhmaṇas already referred to emerged from the privacy of silent prayer still muttering petitionary invocations of God and his incarnations, and started to address the assembly in a voice which only slowly accelerated to audibility. "Lords Buddha and Mahāvīra, Masters Ajita and Makkhali, assembled scholars and noble ladies and gentlemen," he said, but noticing that he had omitted reference to śūdras and ādivāsīs in attendance, quickly added "and others," and made the following submission:

> The Tathāgata's breath-taking and liberating identification of Ātman and Śūnyatā, self and nothingness, is a complete upaniṣad, a 'Bṛhadāraṇyaka upaniṣad' or 'Great Forest upaniṣad,' and would have been recognized and received as such by the custodians of Vedic revelation had the tradition of revelatory truth-seeing and truth-receiving not been in the state of stagnation in which it is today; and had sectarian loyalties not been as divisive as they are today and as they are likely to remain, despite striking examples of sects-transcending togetherness in inquiry, as in this assembly, set by sages like the Buddha and Mahāvīra and scholars of different persuasions. And yet I know that I am not the only Brāhmaṇa present here who would like to offer salutations to Lord Buddha for the blessed light he has thrown on the much misunderstood truth of Advaita Vedānta, the truth of the ultimacy of self and the urgency of self-realization, and on the much misunderstood truth of nothingness and nirvāṇa which is at the heart of his own distinctive teaching.
>
> However, I am by family tradition a paurāṇika, a reciter and interpreter of sacred stories and histories and myths and symbols; and I would like to express my profound vocational and personal gratitude to the Tathāgata for the mythological instructiveness of his discourse at this assembly, if I may be permitted to shock as I know I do some of his more demythologizing followers. I here allude not only to the Buddha's elucidation of Śiva the destroyer's unexpected sustaining role in creation, with the implied warning to future humanity against the temptation of robbing material reality of the apocalyptic energy stored away in its secret recesses, like the primeval poison in Śiva's throat. I refer also, and especially, to the Tathāgata's defense of Lord Mahāvīra against Master Ajita which took the form of a compassionate acknowledgment of the ecological restraint which characterizes non-human life's apparently relent-

> lessly violent struggle for survival. Although there is no explicit mythological dimension to this insight of the Tathāgata, its implications opened my eyes to the deep meaning of the separation of Rāma and Sītā in the Rāmāyaṇa; and healed my heart of the terrible hurt inflicted on it by Master Ajita's suggestion that Rāma's abandonment of Sītā implies the abandonment by truth, i.e. Rāma, of life's energy, i.e. Sītā; of life itself.
>
> I do not know if humanity in a few thousand years will or will not destroy itself along with all life on earth, but the Buddha has enabled me to see that the impulse for such holocaust cannot come from Rāma and Sītā. Sacred mythology and history may not succeed in preserving life on earth, but they are not against it. Let me tell you and myself again some Rāmāyaṇa stories in a new light, by the grace of Śrī Rāma, Śrī Sītā, Śrī Lakṣmaṇa and Hanumān, to explain what I mean; and by the grace also of the Buddha and Mahāvīra.

Despite some derisive yawning by Ajita and simultaneous snapping of fingers by Makkhali, the attention of the torch-lit assembly under the big tree and a full moon, which had by now moved to a more angular position in relation to the banyan, was riveted to what the Brāhmaṇa was saying; and all, regardless of caste and status in society, like modern Indian viewers of television Rāmāyaṇa and Mahābhārata serials, waited impatiently like children to hear the paurāṇika's retelling of Rāmāyaṇa episodes in the light of the Buddha's ecological observations. Some forest-dwellers in Ananyā's camp whose ancestors, like hers, had preserved and passed down the generations many a non-mainstream Rāmāyaṇa story, were especially excited and stood up, as did Ananyā, so as to see and hear the story-teller better. The two young kṣatriya ladies who had joined Ananyā in sympathy remained seated on either side of her, holding her hands in a triangular formation of casteless comradeship; they were no less eager than the others to hear the stories.

The paurāṇika continued, after a few moments of meditation with closed eyes and folded hands in which other Brāhmaṇas joined him, as follows:

> The story of the Rāmāyaṇa begins with its narrator, the sage Vālmīki, watching in ecstatic amazement the love play of a pair of krauñca birds on the branch of a tree, symbolizing the joyous unity which is at the heart of the nature of things: the ānanda or bliss from which alone creation can proceed. What a profound spiritual tribute this scene is to non-human life, to its

scriptural status and to the ecological worthiness of its reproductive continuity, as I see for the first time now! Savor this scene, my friends; but wait, here comes the speeding arrow of a hunter and it plunges into the heart of the female bird, killing her instantly and knocking her off the branch of the tree of life, leaving the male bird panting and wailing inconsolably. Cruel, cruel, fate! He Rāma, He Sītā!

Violating the hunter's code, a human being has killed a mating creature, and a curse spontaneously issues from the sage's lips condemning the hunter to a life of unceasing and unquiet wandering. Sages are not meant to curse, or to curse so harshly, and Vālmīki is filled with remorse; but he finds that the metrical rhythm of his verse of curse is hauntingly beautiful, and is urged by the Creator, Brahmā himself, to compose the Rāmāyaṇa story in that meter and rhythm.

I see as clearly as daylight tonight, strange though this sounds, that the moral of this foundational Rāmāyaṇa episode is that condemnation of ecological crime cannot be too harsh and that ecological sensitivity alone can provide the rhythm of language and thought necessary for telling and understanding the story of the divine couple Rāma and Sītā; and in the light of this revelation let me offer, by the grace of my paurāṇika ancestors, some reflections on the abduction[23] and so-called abandonment[24] of Sītā: two episodes from the Rāmāyaṇa which, along with others, have troubled but kept alive the moral sensibility of our society.

During the period of their banishment, Rāma and Sītā and Lakṣmaṇa are forest hunters who take animal life only when this is unavoidable for survival, and live on fruits and roots when it is possible to do so: observing strictly the ecological code of hunting and thus establishing or revealing a perfect harmony of all forms of life in the divine nature.

If I may make a small digression permitted by the code of story-telling, and in the light of the Tathāgata's illuminating discourse on self-realization and emptiness, it suddenly occurs to me that the special unity of Rāma and Sītā as the divine couple surely represents the indivisible intimacy and intensity of self-realized self-consciousness; and Lakṣmaṇa, Śeṣa, who is not other than Rāma and Sītā except in the playful camouflage of world-appearance, is the limitless witnessing consciousness of the divine nature, the unbounded space within which all possibilities manifest, emptiness and nothingness, the shape of nirvāṇa. But I am a paurāṇika, and I must not dwell in the territory of Vedantic exegesis too long, although its current stagnation tempts me often to trespass into it.

The divine threesome—Rāma, Sītā, Lakṣmaṇa—are much happier in the forest in ecological harmony with nature, than they were in Ayodhyā riddled with the disharmony of court and palace intrigue. So there they are in their forest home one afternoon, which is luminous with their and nature's radiance, seated in the little verandah of their thatched hut; having recently enjoyed, with gratitude to life's generosity, and without gluttony or guilt, a meal of venison.

Now suddenly enters into the narrative and Sītā's field of vision an incomparably beautiful deer with silver spots on its golden skin, but who is in reality Mārīca,[25] a demon kinsman of the demon king Rāvaṇa, as you will recall. Rāvaṇa's demon vandals have for a long time been destroying the forest's creatures and trees, enslaving its ādivāsīs, and disturbing the austerities of its sages and even killing and eating them up! Sinful violations of the integrity of a forest, araṇya, that perfect image of the peace of ātman and emptiness, self-realization and nirvāṇa. Nārāyaṇa! Nārāyaṇa!

As the storyteller ritually paused in anguish at his own description of the desecration of a forest in antiquity, shame filled the hearts and bent the heads of some of the noblemen and ladies who had done exactly that when they rode horses and elephants wildly and tramplingly through a contemporary forest during their recent fateful hunt for a missing slave girl; and Ananyā's new friends covered their faces with their hands and wept. It was Ananyā's turn to comfort them.

Understood superficially, the paurāṇika continued, the narrative here notes that Sītā longed desperately to possess the deer's golden skin as a garment and, disregarding Rāma's suspicion that the animal might be a demon in disguise, forced him to go and hunt it down; and when Rāma did not return for a long time, she forced Lakṣmaṇa, again against his own better judgement, to go in search of Rāma. The absence of both Rāma and Lakṣmaṇa from the scene gave Rāvaṇa the opportunity he was looking for. Disguised as a mendicant, he lured Sītā out of a protective zone marked out for her by Lakṣmaṇa, and revealing his demon form, forcibly took her away in his flying chariot all the way to Laṅkā; precipitating war and necessitating all the other fateful occurrences of the Rāmāyaṇa, all the way up to the abandonment of Sītā by Rāma, her descent into the earth,[26] and Rāma's apparently suicidal immersion into the Sarayū's currents.[27]

Dear friends, I have been enabled tonight to divine the epic's meaning more deeply. All three of them, Rāma, Lakṣmaṇa, and Sītā, must have known in their omniscient hearts who the golden deer really was, and that it was necessary to destroy it to defeat Rāvaṇa's designs upon the truth and power of the forest, regardless of consequences; for without forests there can be no blossoming (instructive botanical metaphor, don't you think?) of life and civilization on earth.

But there was a cruel dilemma involved here. For although the deer was a demon in disguise who merited death, the disguise had all the perfection of appearance; and at the level of appearance at which ordinary humanity lives, killing the animal would count as a violation of the hunter's code which forbade the taking of life beyond the necessity of nourishment, and remember our trinity had just finished a meal of deer flesh. And whether justifiably or not, killing any creature unavoidably leaves disconsolate at least its mate or mother or young offspring, a tragedy worth preventing whenever possible. And yet the consequences of letting Mārīca go would have been unacceptably cataclysmic.

I see it clearly now, that Rāma, Sītā and Lakṣmaṇa decide to violate the hunter's code phenomenologically, i.e. to all appearances, rather than see life and civilization undermined by the fury of Rāvaṇa. And they are willing phenomenologically to pay the price for their apparent ecological indiscipline, so great is the importance of such discipline to the nature of things and the integrity of life. Thus it is that at the level of appearance, Sītā is abducted by Rāvaṇa; and at the end of the war, citizens of Ayodhyā are able to doubt her fidelity to Rāma in view of her long incarceration in Laṅkā. Morally yes, but phenomenologically, even this suspicion cannot be faulted. And Sītā is forsaken by Rāma.

Rāma abandons Sītā ostensibly because of his subjects' skepticism regarding her chastity. But I see undeniably tonight that victory and reunion had not made Rāma and Sītā forget the killing of the golden deer, nor the price that has to be paid for the ecological violation which that killing constitutes at the level of appearance. For the unecological killing of any creature not merely constitutes the badness of avoidable slaughter, it also means grief and privation and isolation for dependent creatures. Thus it is in kārmic reparation that Rāma and Sītā separate, and in order to strengthen the credibility of the ecological lesson they want their subjects and humanity in general to learn, they are obliged to go through the rituals of banishment and fire-tests with phenomenologically terrifying similitude.

But there is redemption for the world here. Sītā's banishment to the forest is in reality Rāma's gift to the forest of divine energy and attention, to remind all generations of humanity that when we honor the ecological integrity of a forest, we honor divine energy; and that we dishonor this energy when we desecrate forests. Rāma reigns in Ayodhyā, for the city too is an ingredient of importance in the divine scheme; but Sītā resides in the forests which makes it possible for civilization to survive and flourish in the city.

Friends, bear with me as I share with you a few more Rāmāyaṇa illuminations with which I have been blessed tonight by the Buddha's discourse and by Mahāvīra's silence. While reminding us of the deadly poison which Śiva held in his throat protectively for the sake of creation, the Tathāgata also spoke of the apocalyptic energy stored away in the recesses of material reality. Unexploited for greed and terror, this energy sustains creation but can equally annihilate it if sought to be robbed from its atomic trustees.

I see the disappearance of Sītā into the bowels of the earth as a powerful underscoring of this fact, and also of the truth that material causality too is not without the divine leavening of self-restraint, chastity, another fundamental truth to which the Buddha graciously drew our attention. Sītā resides not only in all the species of life of which the forest is a trustee, she breathes also in the interstices of invisible matter. What a consolation!

All things pass, as the Buddha teaches. Śrī Rāma's voluntary ending of his earthly sojourn by immersion in the speedily flowing Sarayū river powerfully expresses this truth of flux, the inexorable passage into nothingness of all things great and small. But this passage, when it is the passing of an avatāra or a sage from the human scene, is surely the highlighting of the continuity of self-realization and emptiness, which is nirvāṇa. By the grace of the Tathāgata and my ancestors, I now see this deeper aspect of the apparently tragic suicide of Rāma by drowning: and I am profoundly consoled.

Master Ajita's strictures against Śrī Kṛṣṇa's role in the Mahābhārata are as shattering of the self-confidence of a traditional paurāṇika like myself as were his castigations of Śrī Rāma. But I am confident that deeper inquiry would restore faith in Śrī Kṛṣṇa as assuredly as, with the help of the Tathāgata's insights, my faith in Śrī Rāma has been wholly restored.

But I do not yet see my way clearly around the moral and spiritual difficulties implied in Master Ajita's criticism of Kṛṣṇa; and in any case I have taken so much of your time. Thank you for bearing with me, and for enabling me to play, however inadequately, something of the role of a traditional storyteller of the sacred before such a distinguished assembly. Jaya Rāma, Jaya Sītā!

VI

A playful breeze had blown throughout the duration of the paurāṇika's discourse, easing the fatigue of concentrated listening. But it had lulled Ajita into sleep and in fact the Keśakambalin had slept right through most of the Rāmāyaṇa exegesis; and Makkhali, though awake, had provided accompanying snoring sounds to dramatize his comrade's and his own indifference to the paurāṇika's labors of reinterpretation. Amazingly, however, just as the paurāṇika had awakened from contemplative prayer at a point of time favorable for his discourse to commence, Ajita awakened now from his sleep with a start and sat up; and with an awareness of what had been said while he slept which can only be called psychic, mumbled the following protest almost like obscenities under his breath:

Enough is enough, boring Brāhmaṇa: you do not, because you *will* not, see, that the fantasticality of demonic and divine and human and animal engagement which is the Rāmāyaṇa story cannot throw the slightest bit of light on the starkly self-centered reality of human life as it is today, and as it will increasingly be with the passage of centuries: the alienated species poised for a perception of the attraction of nothingness and a heroic fight into it in a not too distant millennium. It is the Mahābhārata, that unclutteredly human story, about which you have been so deceivingly silent, which unmasks the duplicity of divinity and the meaninglessness of morality and secretly celebrates the frenzy of self-destruction. Enough is enough.

It would have been pointless to point out to Ajita that his silencing formula "enough is enough" is also a powerful picture of self-restraint, the blessed temperance of life, matter, and nothingness — not to mention the utter frugality of singular self-consciousness — that the Buddha, and inspired by him, the Brāhmaṇa, had been talking about. Ajita was bitter and hoped desperately to defeat all optimism in the assembly by confronting it with the slaughter of Kurukṣetra, and the self-destruction of the Yādavas.

The insulted paurāṇika merely shook his head in disbelief and disagreement but felt brutally put down, and then he suddenly noticed Mahāvīra's right hand raised in abhaya mudrā, especially for him, as it seemed, and was deeply comforted by the gesture. And even Ajita's psychic powers could not have anticipated where the challenge to his challenge was going to come from.

It came from a former persecutor of Ananyā, converted to compassion and moved to contrition by the wisdom of the Buddha and the heartlessness of Ajita: the pensive kṣatriya princess sitting next to Ananyā on her right, Viśvapriyā, 'darling of the world' being the meaning of her name, who spoke thus:

> I am a Yādava woman, Master Ajita, a descendant of the few surviving families of Śrī Kṛṣṇa's clan which virtually annihilated itself in insensate drunken rage some years after the near total destruction of all combatants in the great Kurukṣetra war.[28] Śrī Kṛṣṇa is our family deity, more so than Śrī Rāma, but also Śrī Rāma, because Rāma and Kṛṣṇa are one in two incarnations; and I was deeply, deeply, offended by your nihilist mischaracterization of these two avatāras of Viṣṇu the sustainer and savior of the world. However, clan elders have often confessed to me, that ever since the ancient carnage of Kurukṣetra, a weariness and distrust of the nature of things has entered the kṣatriya soul which often makes us eager to believe that the consuming violence of war may be rooted in some fundamental flaw in nature, some svadharma of self-destruction at the heart of evanescent existence. I was overcome by this weariness just when I wanted to walk out of this assembly in protest against your attribution of moral cowardice to Rāma and of amoral destructiveness to Kṛṣṇa; and so I stayed, numbed by doubt.
>
> You fueled this doubt further when, addressing Ananyā, you spoke of our jewelry which she had taken as representing the foolish optimism of those who think paltry existence had any chance against omnivorous nothingness, filling to the brim my cup of despair. Then came the unexpectedly corrective shock of your astounding accusation that the Buddha had robbed Ananyā of what you described as her true ornament, her cynical smile. This was a compound falsehood for which I cannot be too grateful to you, Master Ajita; for it reminded me

of the Tathāgata's compassion toward me and other persecutors of Ananyā, and also toward Ananyā, and stirred in me and my sister Lopāmudrā a surging love for Ananyā and all those who are regarded as inferior human beings, indeed as less than human beings, by our society. We were propelled by a power greater than that of ownership of property and people to come and sit by the side of Ananyā, losing pride and recovering self-respect.

I also felt less offended by you than I had been. I even felt compassion for you, if you don't mind my saying so, Master Ajita, because I realized how poorly you, who read the future, read the faces of women: a common failing of ascetics, though not of sages. Perhaps your mother didn't love you or look at you sufficiently uncalculatingly to enable you to chart the shifting currents of feeling which manifest all over a woman's face. Ananyā's haunting smile can be a simultaneously submissive, threatening, pleading and plotting signature of her soul, and is also heavy with weariness: but not cynicism, no, that is not the meaning of her smile or the message of her face. You've got her all wrong.

It is we, high-born kṣatriya and Brāhmaṇa men and women, who so constantly wear a cynical smile of superiority in relation not only to the low born, but also in relation to one another, such is the arrogance of ego in us. Power undermines the plasticity of the face.

Our cynicism is in regard to any claim to a privilege greater than that of power—political or ecclesiastical—made by or on behalf of any one who is not a sage or an avatāra; and indeed while such cynicism does ensure against credulousness and the adulation of spiritual mediocrity, it frequently denies us access to authentic greatness, not only of unrecognized sages and misunderstood avatāras, but also of such things as compassion and charity and forbearance and forgiveness which are far greater than political or ecclesiastical power.

I am aware, Master Ajita, that your and Master Makkhali's cynicism extends to all these things and is unsparing also of sages and avatāras: but as a student of abhinaya, expressive symbolism, in sacred dance and sculpture, I doubt if anyone—even you—can smile in an all-comprehensively cynical way: and you don't, bless your mother.

May Mahādeva forgive us, but some of us recently approached the Buddha himself in this forest with cynical smiles of superiority and arrogant unbelief in his intellectual and moral and spiritual authority, of which we had heard; and rudely asked him if he had seen Ananyā the thief around, heard her cries, perhaps seen her body half-devoured by a carnivore, etc.

Viśvapriyā's face contorted in anguish as she recalled the episode and couldn't proceed any further. Ananyā linked arms with her and Lopāmudrā, and a current of mutual forgiveness and gratitude flowed through their bodies as they saw the Buddha's upraised right hand in abhaya mudrā offering the blessing of fearlessness and forgiveness to all who suffer and seek the end of suffering in liberation from ego. His eyes were closed in samādhi and filled with tears of compassion for all sorrowing and diminishing existence.

The princess continued:

The Tathāgata asked us why we were looking for a slave and not seeking the self. There was an upsetting magic to this illuminating counter-question which considerably shook our cynical self-confidence. For to seek a slave is to descend into dependence, the slave being no more dependent on her masters than they are on her, and not at all an advance towards independence or real freedom which can only be of self-knowledge or self-realization which is dependent only on itself, like the sky of emptiness which is enclosed only by itself.

But wasn't it right to chase a thief who had run off with our identifying possession, our precious jewelry? No it wasn't, we understood from the wordless compassion of the Buddha's abhaya. For if the jewelry was ours through inheritance and possession, the wealth it represented was no less Ananyā's, because it could not have been created without the toil of generations of slaves like herself. And as we were unlikely to share this wealth with her and other producers of it, she wasn't quite unjustified in decamping with it.

What we had truly lost, and which was wholly ours, was self-knowledge. Not the knowledge that we were the aristocracy, for with the loss of the jewelry we had ceased to be aristocrats and become predators hunting a human being in utter violation of the noblest of codes, the ecological code of the forest adhered to by flesh-eating no less than by grass-eating creatures: most of the time, anyway. As soon as we realized this implication of the Buddha's compassionately admonitory instruction in self-inquiry, many of us entirely lost our cynical smiles. We were humbled by truth, by the truth of ourselves; a large number of us, anyway. You cannot restore to us that foolish smirk of false identity, Master Ajita: it was as ugly as it was unreal.

Of course Ananyā returned the jewelry to us, and we returned to her her freedom, obeying the Tathāgata's wordless command in this regard. But the words 'returned' and 'restored' hardly capture the spirit of the equation wrought by him in our consciousness.

The Tathāgata had given Ananyā a length of saffron cloth torn from the hem of his own holy garment at her request, out of which she made a pouch, and it was this pouch containing all our jewels that she gave us back as a womb of wisdom, a sacrament of symbolism: the gathering saffron representing ethical sensitivity and ecological restraint, the framework of civilization within which alone human life like all life and nature and matter can glow like the gathered jewels with the light of self-realization and nirvāṇa. Ananyā had drawn us mysteriously to the Buddha, and brought back from him this liberating message. How can we speak of restoring liberty to one who was instrumental in liberating us from bondage to a false view of nobility, of ourselves?

Lost in the ecstasy of excluding love we were, having cast Ananyā out of the sphere of justice and partnership. How unlike the Rāsa Līlā[29] of Śrī Kṛṣṇa in Vṛndāvana which also timelessly takes place every night of the full moon, i.e. under the sponsorship of enlightenment. Śrī Kṛṣṇa's līlā leaves no one out in the cold, every Gopī has him as her partner; implying, as I am beginning to understand in the light of the Buddha's and the learned paurāṇika's discourses under tonight's full moon, that no one is without the companionship of self-realization and none falls outside the sphere of emptiness' compassion, outside the sky's blue umbrella of protection and accommodation.

Rāma and Kṛṣṇa are one, both of them sky-blue, and the compassion of Rāma so movingly described by the paurāṇika cannot be absent in Kṛṣṇa. Only the idiom changes in the Mahābhārata from the Rāmāyaṇa's wide and unvarying attention to all categories of being to one of focused concentration on imperiled humanity: your very own preferred idiom, Master Ajita. (The *Bhāgavatam*,[30] of course, like most of the Rāmāyaṇa, remains quite uncompromisingly green in its ecology and geology and theology). And yet, in at least one of its most dramatic episodes, the Mahābhārata encodes an integrated lesson in ecology and ethics with a terrifying reference, and not only relevance, to the fate of the earth.

Makkhali and Ajita had for some time now been playing a game of dice at which Makkhali, through cheating, was contriving continuously to lose to Ajita, in the hope thereby of cheering him up; for Ajita was paying disguised but close auditory and psychic attention to Viśvapriyā's powerfully unfolding repudiation of his repudiation of the availability of the Mahābhārata to life's hopes on earth, his face twitching with anxiety about anxiety's chances against advaita.

"I refer to the game of dice," announced Viśvapriyā, causing Ajita and Makkhali to turn gleefully in her direction because they thought she was launching an objection to their private game. They would have loved this to have been the case, as it would have given Ajita a splendid opportunity to interrupt her and draw attention to the heavily loaded dice of entropy cast against optimism in the game of existence; and so on. They were quickly disappointed, however, as Viśvapriyā went on to explain what she was referring to.

> I refer to the game of dice[31] in the court of the blind patriarch Dhṛtarāṣṭra, at which, having first staked and lost all his wealth and then his own and his four brothers' freedom, Yudhiṣṭhira, the eldest Pāṇḍava, finally stakes Draupadī—common wife of all the five brothers—and loses her too, thanks to the cheating prowess of Śakuni who plays on behalf of the wicked Duryodhana.
>
> At the command of Duryodhana, Duḥśāsana proceeds to disrobe Draupadī who, like her husband, has now become a slave of the Kauravas. No one intervenes to stop this unprecedented unrighteousness: not the old King, none of the learned and heroic elders present, not even her husbands. Draupadī has no one but the physically absent yet omnipresent Śrī Kṛṣṇa to turn to in prayer in her heart, and so she does. Kṛṣṇa frustrates Duḥśāsana's evil intention by miraculously extending the length of Draupadī's sārī beyond Duḥśāsana's violating capabilities. Her honor is protected. And the stage is set for the rest of the momentous events in the epic story. But the ethico-ecological instructiveness of this episode is unmatched by anything else in the Mahābhārata.
>
> The five Pāṇḍava brothers represent the five natural elements: earth, water, fire, air and space, i.e. the whole range of terrestrial existence and its spatial setting—matter, nature, non-human and human life in space. 'Space' as a natural element is not the environing emptiness of the limitless sky but the

nearness and remoteness of entities and collectivities, the territoriality of established orders of life, the realms of privacy and the sovereignties of society. And Draupadī represents the principle of ecological harmony to which all five elements of terrestrial reality are married in their undisturbed state. Ecology and ethics cannot be too sharply distinguished in this sacrament of marriage. Ecology being non-anthropocentric ethics; and ethics, anthropocentric ecology. Peace and joy and love are the progeny of this marriage.

In violation especially of the ethical demands of equality and freedom, human beings constantly seek to dominate one another as individuals and groups and to control the wealth of the earth. This can lead, as an extreme possibility, to the near total domination of all humanity and all of the earth's resources by an oppressive minority. The gambling away by Yudhiṣṭhira of all his wealth and his and his brothers' freedom to the cheating Kauravas dramatizes this extreme possibility as a warning to future and contemporary humanity; and also hints that loss of freedom results from the lack of vigilance of victims too, and not only because of the superior strength of would-be tyrants.

But the Mahābhārata episode of the attempted disrobing of Draupadī hints at the possibility of an even greater crisis than political subjugation. Slaves can always hope to rebel and overthrow tyranny. This may take long but is always a perfectly conceivable possibility. But if along with the enslavement of humanity, and with the collusion or because of the indifference of human populations, tyranny begins also to dishonor the ecological compact of existence and starts to denude the earth of its resources, then God alone can save the earth, as Kṛṣṇa saved Draupadī when, taking advantage of the unprotesting and unprotecting silence of the Pāṇḍavas and others, Duḥśāsana attempted to strip her naked.

Kṛṣṇa's miraculous help came at the eleventh hour and it was very narrowly that Draupadī, or the biosphere, escaped irredeemable degradation. Perhaps this episode symbolically encapsulates human memory of a remote time in the past when the earth's forest cover (Draupadī's sārī) had begun rapidly to disappear due to some gigantic natural calamity or due to demonic depredatoriness, such as Rāvaṇa's in the Rāmāyaṇa: and a miraculous sustained stretch of rainfall resurrected the forests. But the message of the Draupadī episode is that this may have been a one-time divine intervention to save an endangered and violated earth which may not be repeated if the crisis recurs as a consequence of unrepentant humanity's escalating disregard of ecological discipline. The episode shows Kṛṣṇa's deep compassion for life and civilization on earth, and also his stern warning that his help cannot be taken for granted by an ungratefully lapsing human species.

Earlier I had spoken of the weariness of the kṣatriya soul since the slaughter of Kurukṣetra and the subsequent near total self-slaughter of the Yādavas. This weariness is something I too feel in my bones, although I am a woman, and family elders and heroes of the battlefield frequently talk about it. The phenomenon isn't, however, pacifism, I am afraid, the view—often attributed rightly or wrongly to the Buddha and Mahāvīra—that war is not justified under any circumstances. Human memory of man's brutal inhumanity to man is too long, and the kṣatriya's pledge to prevent and deterrently avenge such inhumanity too strong, for him to be persuaded by doctrinaire pacifism to lay down arms and belittle the entire past of soldiering humanity: all the horrors of war notwithstanding.

As his daughter and sister, potential spouse and mother, I can see that the kṣatriya hero's war-weariness springs rather from the realization that the complexity of evolving human society and technology is such that not even a just war can any longer be fought with honor even by the just. The luxury of even a moderately clean war is no longer available to the noblest warlords. Such was the case even with the Mahābhārata war. The old gallantries of limited tribal warfare were laughably unobservable in the context of the deadliness of new weaponry and the novelties of battle formations and the immensely complex consequences of victory or defeat.

The Pāṇḍavas could not abjectly surrender to the Kauravas and leave the earth to the mercy of human equivalents of mutants and demons. Nor could they hope to defeat the Kauravas with their hands tied to their backs by inapplicable rules of gallantry, as Kṛṣṇa knew. It is only by the grace and encouragement of the divine Śrī Kṛṣṇa that a narrow victory accrues to the Pāṇḍavas after an inevitably brutally fought and unavoidably rules—flouting battle. The Pāṇḍavas barely survive. Arjuna's gallant son Abhimanyu is ungallantly, immorally, slaughtered; and the Pāṇḍavas' only surviving descendant, Parīkṣita, is a mortally wounded foetus in Abhimanyu's widow Uttarā's womb, and is miraculously saved by Kṛṣṇa.

It is again by the grace of Kṛṣṇa that some Yādavas survive the clan's self-slaughtering spree several years after the Kurukṣetra war. I see divine compassion and warning in all this, not annihilationist destructiveness, Master Ajita. Both historically and symbolically, again a one-time divine intervention to ensure the defeat of demonic lust for power and destructiveness and the bare survival of the Pāṇḍavas whose gambling propensity — lack of vigilance, complacency — had dangerously strengthened the Kauravas. Call tyranny's and greed's bluff in time, Śrī Kṛṣṇa seems to be saying, for he may not kārmically be able to intervene a second time.

And call modern warfare's bluff too, Kṛṣṇa is saying to those who can hear: it has lost aboriginal innocence, it is not an honorable game any more, it cannot frame rules which it will not flout. Prevent war, therefore, not because war has always been wrong, but because it can never be gallant again. This is the profoundest disincentive to war-making and war-mongering that I can think of. Humanity may not heed Śrī Kṛṣṇa's warning or recall his salvationally iconoclastic intervention in history, and may indeed perish and cause all life to perish as you prophesy, Master Ajita; but do not, O do not, slander the cowherd of Vṛṇdāvana and the lover of humanity who cared more for the survival of life and peace and joy on earth than antiquated rules of prehistoric war games!

Handed down to my family by Yādava ancestors and their paurāṇika preceptors is yet another symbolic reading of the Mahābhārata. The five Pāṇḍavas are the five senses of knowledge in celebratorily polyandrous marriage to unitary mind, Draupadī; and senses and mind can together be surrendered, as the Pāṇḍavas and Draupadī were, to the self which the Tathāgata rightly asks us to seek; and which is 'Kṛṣṇa,' darkness of the intimacy of self-realization and of the 'extinguishedness' of ego which is nirvāṇa or emptiness. Thus surrendered to self, the senses and mind can be victorious over a hundred objects of distraction and temptation, the Kauravas, distractions of greed and temptations of annihilation. However, when the senses and mind are not surrendered to self or emptiness, they are like the mass and leaders of humanity who long to live for the sake of their lives alone, and not for the sake of life as such and as a whole and its truth: and soon succumb to the temptation of despair and self-destruction like Śrī Kṛṣṇa's ungrateful, unseeing, Yādava clan.

The isolationism of ego, individual or collective, dangerously caricatures the autonomy of self-realization and may fulfill your prophecy of doom, ascetic Master of absurdism; but blame us, including yourself, and not the nature of things and nothingness, nor the meaning and message of sacred history and mythology.

Viśvapriyā ended her testimony with these words. Lopāmudrā embraced her sister in a poignant gesture of remembrance of kṣatriya agony and ecstasy. Kṣatriya-born themselves, the Buddha and Mahāvīra caught each other's eye in a blessed moment of joint and grateful remembrance of their mothers.

VII

The paurāṇika had heard Viśvapriyā's energetic exegesis of Mahābhārata episodes with a twinge of envy, because it was she and not he who had risen to the defense of Śrī Kṛṣṇa against Ajita's calumny. But his spirits were revived by a wondrous thought which literally waylaid him: the kinship of Kṛṣṇa and Kṛṣṇā (another name of Draupadi's), dark mysteries of selfhood and the mind of emptiness, anticipating the kinship of advaita and the Buddha. He coughed in readiness to intervene; but as happens so often at conferences, he wasn't able to do so because something like a "coffee-break" was now indicated, with the usual opportunities for natural necessities; and this was announced by the nihilist masters' synchronized yawning, stretching, ritual of standing up and slow march towards some far bushes, followed at a distance of respect by a torch-bearer because moonlight had considerably scattered by now and its source concealed behind high ranges of trees.

More torches were lit, more servants pressed into service by the command of aristocratic eyes. Fresh spring water and an assortment of forest fruits—figs, berries, custard apples, bananas—gathered earlier were partaken of by nearly everyone, but not by Mahāvīra and his group of monastic followers who adhered to their strict rule of not eating or drinking anything after sunset and before sunrise; nor by the Buddha and his followers who ate only one meal a day in the afternoon. Cupped hands served as vessels into which drinking water was poured in a slow and steady stream from earthen pitchers by servants.

Ananyā begged to be allowed, and was allowed, to do this service for the Tathāgata, whose beautiful long cupped begging hands were a sight for the Gods as he, the giver of living waters, knelt before a recently freed slave girl to slake ordinary but universal thirst. Fireflies ringed his and her head in adoration.

Viśvapriyā and Lopāmudrā lit several clay lamps and placed them in niches made generously available by the lower, arm-like sagging branches of the banyan; but out of fear and respect they did not thus illuminate the space around the seats of Ajita and Makkhali marked by playing dice and reserved for them. Like the slow-burning torches, clay lamps were essential equipment for nights out in the forest. These lamps had defined areas of privacy on that other night of the full moon when Ananyā had bolted with the ornaments of the lovers' party, provoking ecological violation and spiritual illumination. Tonight Viśvapriyā and Lopāmudrā are moved to put the little luminaries to sacramental use because of the continuous remembrance, both blasphemous and devotional, of Rāma and Kṛṣṇa that has characterized the colloquium. The paurāṇika is overcome with emotion and slowly circumambulates the lamp-lit tree, chanting "Rāma, Rāma, Kṛṣṇā, Kṛṣṇā."

Everybody soon returned to their place and nearly all seemed moved by the new stage-setting for the concluding phase of the seminar, suggestive of the dawning of flickers of hope in the midst of growing darkness; and honoring the tree of life firmly rooted in matter below and, invertedly, in emptiness above. Not Ajita and Makkhali, of course; the former produced a lengthy sequence of sneering sneezes, and the latter went around with folded hands offering mock obeisance to the lamps. As soon as Makkhali returned to his place beside Ajita, the Keśakambalin made the following dark observations.

> Makkhali is indeed quite justified in offering his homage to those little lights of ego, fireflies of foolish hope. Notwithstanding all the adoration of ambiguous antiquity poured out by Viśvapriyā, all the ecological theology spun out of thin metaphysics and thick mythology by her and the pitiable paurāṇika, all the sophistry of Gotama's speech and all the vanity of Vardhamāna's silence, I have no doubt at all that the foolishnesses of egoistic individuality and the fanaticisms of egoistic collectivity will transform themselves before too long into unflinching annihilationist resolution; and in a manifestation of unprecedented partnership, individuals and collectivities will engineer euthanasia for the earth's life after a spell of uniquely uninhibited indulgence of the impulse to enjoyment and violence. Leavened by the fossils of fallen life, all non-biological existence too will be stirred into climactic collapse, into all-devouring nothingness.
>
> Elegant but foolish sisters, Viśvapriyā and Lopāmudrā, the tree of life will be burnt down precisely by these little lamps of

private light with which you imagine you have honored it; and the resultant fire—beyond history—will also consume the forest of existence. Ephemeral jewelry and immoral slavery are poorly substituted by the delusion of self-realization and the illusion of equality.

You lost nothing and have gained nothing. Nothing! Ah, what a gain that! But enough is enough. The moon has run away like Ananyā with the light the sun had entrusted it with! Forgiven, it will return tomorrow night, contrite and diminished and will waste away for a few more days, then return fattened with confidence and ready to distract and deceive again. The unself-deceiving light of mind that it is, the moon knows that the self—the Sun—is dying; and that the empty sky of our days and nights — nirvāṇa's accommodatingness! — is but a bubble within the limitlessness of cold nothingness. This is why the moon plays tramp and truant and allows itself to be hidden by clouds presaging the death of earth, moon, and sun; life, mind and self and their limited space of possibilities.

Let Ananyā represent the mocking truth of mind and the moon and disown all suns and skies, all wombs and worlds; let her conclude this colloquium before sneaking sunlight stabs her in the back and darkens her heart with deceiving hope.

Once again Ajita's nihilism was soliciting Ananyā's aboriginality. Modern weariness, for that is what nihilism is, is easily able to browbeat moral romanticism and even confuse fledgling spiritual awakening, but Viśvapriyā's revived paurāṇika and kṣatriya self-knowledge was made of much sterner stuff and Ajita chose to leave well alone the thrust of her repudiation of his reviling caricature of mythological wisdom. Nor could he hope, in his concluding intervention, to trounce the Tathāgata and the Tīrthaṃkara.

Ajita desperately needed to win aboriginality's, antiquity's, Ananyā's support for annihilationism against the patience of timeless wisdom represented by the Buddha and Mahāvīra and the power of civilizational self-confidence represented by the ethically and ecologically sensitive revivalism of Viśvapriyā and the paurāṇika. He needed to bully, flatter, seduce, the pride of prehistory represented by Ananyā into rebellion against future time, against time itself.

Proselytizing self-destructiveness is profoundly disturbed by happy longevity and would dearly wish it to be seduced by euthanasia's false promise of eternal rest. It is no coincidence that aboriginal peoples are the first victims of the secretly suicidal vandalism of what passes as modern civilization. But let us return to the consummatory phase of Ajita's forest inquisition.

Ananyā did not feel inclined or obliged to respond to Ajita's presumptuous command to her to conclude the colloquium with an apology for annihilationism. Besides, she had noticed the restiveness of a particular young prince who sat with some of his companions not too far from Ajita and Makkhali, a proximity expressive of free-thinking youth's respect for heterodoxy, and whose longing for Lopāmudrā and Lopāmudrā's ambivalent attraction for whom were no secret to Ananyā. 'Parantapa,' commonly understood to mean 'scorcher of foes,' one of the names of the Mahābhārata hero Arjuna, was the young man's name. Both Ananyā and Lopāmudrā darted a "Won't you speak?" look at him; and Parantapa spoke as follows:

> Ananyā has heralded a new day in the lives of many of us, and it is only appropriate that it is with her testimony that this colloquium should conclude when dawn breaks in a little while from now. Most generously she signals her permission to me to speak before her and I promise her that it is she and not I who will bridge this dying night and the morning it is churning into visibility.
>
> The jewel that can never be lost, which is undetachable from ourselves, is the jewel of self-realization, self-knowledge, self-consciousness. Just as the circumambient emptiness of nirvāṇa—of which the sky Master Ajita decries is a stunning symbol—is the kingdom from which we can never be banished, being the limitless range of self-realization. Likewise, the freedom that cannot be taken away from anyone is the timeless autonomy of self. However, this truth of self-knowledge and freedom, this self-knowledge of freedom and truth, lies deeply self-obscured in our culture and consciousness. This self-obscuration is a greater loss than the loss of all the kingdoms of all the worlds; and awakening to self-knowledge a greater gain than gaining all these kingdoms.
>
> It has taken the whip-lashing of Master Ajita's nihilism, the disorientating power of Master Makkhali's maneuvers, and the compassionate teachings of the Buddha and Mahāvīra through speech and silence to awaken some of us to the truth of self and emptiness and freedom, however inadequately. I can see that our attachment to our lost jewelry most grotesquely misrepresented the relationship of self to its unrobbable wealth of self-

realization. And our presumptuous ownership and mistreatment of Ananyā was a blasphemous denial of the unenslavability of omnipresent, infinitely-many-centered Ātman. 'Ananyā' literally means 'No other, self,' and we treated her as an *other*, not-self; distorting, instead of imaging, the truth of ourselves and all things and nothingness in our unethical relationship with her.

In the light of the truth of advaita to which the Tathāgata has awakened us, I can see the deeper meaning of my own name, 'Parantapa'; and the deeper meaning of the name 'Lopāmudrā' which adorns the woman I adore, my heart's longing who sits with her sister Viśvapriyā by the side of Ananyā.

Parantapa and Lopāmudrā caught each other's eye in the wavering light of lamps and torches and felt for the first time a strength of constancy flowing from one to the other. Continuing with confidence, Parantapa elaborated:

Clansmen and family members never fail to remind me that 'Parantapa' means 'scorcher of foes,' for that is what the great Arjuna was, 'Parantapa' being a name conferred upon him by Śrī Kṛṣṇa himself during their immortal discourse enshrined in the *Bhagavadgītā*.[32] While this meaning of the name certainly fits Arjuna, the twang of whose Gāṇḍīva was sufficient to scatter his enemies, the deeper meaning of 'Parantapa,' as I can now see, is 'scorcher of otherness,' for otherness,—or apparent otherness, for there is no real otherness—is self's only foe and it is truly scorched in the blazing light of self-realization of which I have had the barest glimpse, thanks to the compassion of the Tathāgata and the blessings of ancestors and preceptors of antiquity and the mysteriousness of destiny.

The apparent otherness of fellow human beings, non-human living beings, non-living matter and nature and environing nothingness melts down in the fire of mokṣa, revealing self's infinite variety of self-images in an ecstatic dance of ethically and ecologically sensitive interdependence and existential autonomy. I can see that this must be the meaning of Śrī Kṛṣṇa's Rāsa Līlā, of which the slaughter of Kurukṣetra and the self-destruction of the Yādavas too are a grotesque and deeply distorted promise.

'Lopāmudrā' means 'the lost ring, now found,' the link of continuity between generations and the seal of relationship between lovers: the hope of life and the honor of civilization on earth deeply obscured in self-forgetfulness, dazzlingly mani-

> fest in self-realization. I can see her whom I love as dramatizing this dawning of hope in the heart of darkness, but only to the extent I am able to live up to my name; to the extent I am able to scale in vision the walls of apparent otherness that divide me from high and low, dead and living, friend or foe, being and nothingness, Buddha and Mahāvīra, Ajita and Makkhali.

Ajita and Makkhali had been fast asleep for some time now, soundlessly partaking of the spirit of night's darkness which would soon evaporate into disquieting dawn. But at the mention of their names by Parantapa, through a mysterious mechanism of clockwork that had worked during the colloquium on earlier occasions also, the two suddenly snored loudly and simultaneously, cockcrowingly, and woke themselves up and sat up rubbing their eyes and yawning. The Eastern sky behind the banyan screened the first faint films of daybreak now over heads of trees, and the moment had arrived for Parantapa to keep his promise and let Ananyā usher in the dawn: and he addressed the following concluding words of his testimony directly to her.

> Ananyā, the night that is now passing had its moments of illumination; and the emerging day will have its darkening shadows. I do not know what the millennia ahead hold for darkness or light, life or death. I do know this, though, that a magical power of truth-seeking has held all of us captive here under this memorable tree since yesterday afternoon. On the night of the previous full moon, the same power drove some of us and you here to the Buddha's presence, compelling widespread self-examination and precipitating this colloquium. You, Ananyā, are the arrow of time that has drawn this circle of space. You must with your testimony dissolve it into time again, yesterday's fixity into the movement of a new day.

VIII

Ananyā stood up and remained silent for several moments with her head bowed and folded hands facing roughly the Buddha and Mahāvīra, more the direction along which they and their companions were dimly visible; and with a sweeping gesture offered obeisance to the assembly as a whole. Then, in a quick inclusive gesture of liberation from otherness and homage to selfhood, she tossed her head up and tied her long hair into a loose knot, brought her hands to rest on her waist, and faced the slowly brightening eastern sky and was lost in thought again for a few moments. And then, fixing her gaze lightly on the flickering flames of some of the lamps, she spoke searchingly as follows:

> Lords Buddha and Mahāvīra, Masters Ajita and Makkhali, learned Brāhmaṇas and noble sires and ladies, and friends. Prince Parantapa has rightly described the preceding fortnight culminating in this assembly as a time of magic. I fear the day that is now unfolding. What will I do with the freedom which was so unexpectedly and mysteriously restored to me a week ago? How can I ever repay the Tathāgata the debt of gratitude that I owe him? Will the special sweet sisterly love which Princesses Viśvapriyā and Lopāmudrā have showered on me survive the harsh social realities of the day?
>
> How long can society suffer inequity without ceasing to be civilization? How many invasions of modernity can forests suffer without ceasing to be sanctuaries of life, aboriginality, and spiritual realization? How many Buddhas and Mahāvīras will it take to dissolve the selfishness of the rich and the powerful and the wrath of the poor and the oppressed into generosity, forgiveness, and responsibility? How many wars will it take to end war? How many animal lives must humanity destroy and devour to win eternal life for itself? And how many sons must women bear to be honored as daughters? How untouchable must the outcaste be not to be raped and killed? Into how many sub-castes must all castes, high and low, divide themselves, all the more perfectly to manifest the indivisibility of selfhood? How ignorant must the ignorant be to melt the hearts of the educated into sharing their knowledge with them, and how unlettered must the illiterate be to deserve to be taught to write and read the names of Gods?[33]

Many heads were lowered in shame, but Ajita's and Makkhali's joy at what they were hearing was irrepressible. Ajita was on his knees, supplicant and wide-eyed, and clapped away as Makkhali mounted his branch invertedly and swayed backwards and forwards in Ananyā's direction with folded hands, whistling a long shrill off-key note of unorthodoxy, daring in its approximation to be an alternative *sa* (the first, śruti or revelatory, note of the octave) which caused premature protesting chirping of birds from all over the tree.

Dark saffron had seeped into the light grey of the sky behind the banyan, its blackness of only a few minutes ago now a memory, not even an after-image: dramatizing the primacy of radiant renunciation in the widening of creation. The chriping continued in response to the advance of light, but the whistling and clapping stopped. Makkhali froze and fell with a thud of despondency, and Ajita frowned in disappointment and abandoned his supplicant posture as Ananyā went on, with emphasis, to add:

> And yet how can weariness alone cause the living to lose faith in life? Is it not in the exhaustion of labor that new life is born? And how can violation presume to undermine the passionate game of love? Or the continuity of life ended merely by the persistence of death? Modernity can insult, deeply wound, aboriginality: but can it lure it into self-destructiveness? Illiteracy cannot prevent the soul from reading the alphabet of self-restraint with which all nature is embroidered and of which environing nothingness is not a devouring denunciation, but the most majestic and sacred letter; and the whisper of 'I, I' in the stoniest heart its most precious syllable.
>
> But how quickly this whisper of truth becomes distorted into the crowing of ego, how easily the generous emptiness of the sky is misread as the vacuity awaiting all life in death and all structure in decomposition! For all I know, Master Ajita may be right in his prophecy of disaster, and ego and exhaustion may indeed invite apocalypse a few thousand years from now, or later, or sooner. But does that possibility make life less worth living now or at any point of time until the holocaust? Does the possibility of a collapse of civilization and the extinction of earthly life entitle us to call civilization itself into question, bring life itself into disrepute, caricature existence and emptiness? 'No!' is what I want vehemently to say today, although even a month ago I would not have known what to say, nor particularly cared to say anything in answer to that question.
>
> I ran off with the jewels and ornaments of my former noble masters and their lady lovers, many of whom are present here, entirely on an impulse, there was no premeditation to the act. How could there have been? Had I reflected on the matter before my legs ran away with me, I would have realized that I had absolutely no chance of escape. Forest communities have become small and scattered and there are informers everywhere, no family would have dared to keep me in hiding for long; and I would have trembled at the very thought of being hunted down like a fox by the vicious hounds and servants usually employed for such a purpose, and I wouldn't have wanted this ancestral forest-womb of aboriginal humanity and all life to be vi-

olated by the invasive violence of elephants and horses who too —as they were—would have been pressed into service to terrify a slave out of her hiding places.

But no action is done merely impulsively. I had felt the deep hurt of being put outside the circle of love that night and the wretchedness of being a watchkeeper, merely, and not the wearer of jewelry. At first I merely wandered away a bit from my depressing post of duty, feeling sorry for myself, not wanting to witness the rejecting game of love. Then I realized—and this realization has deepened during the course of this colloquium — that that circle merely represented the increasingly closed world of dominant contemporary humanity which leaves out of its sphere of justice and concern not only aboriginal communities and untouchable outcastes, but also all non-human life and —this I see with clarity only now—non-living nature and nothingness too. The wealth which bought those ornaments was produced by the labor of the earth as a whole and with the blessings of the sky; and the ornaments, therefore, belonged neither to their possessors, lords and ladies, nor to their slave custodian: but to Mother Earth who manifests and nourishes all creatures and structures of existence and whose halo, as I see now, is the limitless all-encompassing sky of emptiness.

My mother had told me that several hundred miles further east of here, in Ayodhyā, where Śrī Rāma reigned ages ago, there is a sacred site known as Sītā's Kitchen which is where the nourishing power of the Divine Mother is concentrated: offerings, however humble, made to Sītā at that site miraculously pour into every cell of every life and every crevice of every cluster of existence as immortalizing energy, and that members of several generations of our family had undertaken a pilgrimage to Sītā's Kitchen. According to the Rāmāyaṇa tradition of our forest community, the existence and significance of this site was disclosed not by Rāma to the ādivāsī king Guha, but by Guha to Rāma: and that it was here, into the bowels of the earth, that Sītā had descended, where she timelessly was and remains. In the language of non-duality, in which we have all been instructed here by inspired speakers, we would say that the earth is Sītā, vibrant self-realization, set in the endlessly unfurling sky of emptiness which is Rāma.

To return to the story of my flight. Distanced from circumscribed love, I felt that destiny was calling upon me to take the ornaments entrusted to my care (gathered and tied securely into folds of cloth around my waist) as an offering to Sītā's Kitchen in atonement for humanity's escalating sin of exclusion: for all are guilty of closing the doors of conscience and consciousness to inconvenient reality, ārya and ādivāsī alike, in varying degrees. The moment this realization came, I started to run as fast as I could, hoping against hope that I would be able to cross this forest uncaught and endless stretches of treeless fields beyond that, resting and hiding all the way, then find a ferryman to take me across the great Sarayū river to Ayodhyā and there make my offering and lay my weary head down forever at Sītā's feet.

IX

Ananyā's aboriginal reading of the significance of Ayodhyā was greeted by the sudden first appearance just above and behind the banyan of a perfectly round, orange, playful sun. This sacred coincidence caused the paurāṇika to stand up tremblingly, and with tears streaming down his cheeks, the bhakta repeatedly uttered the chant "Rāma, Lakṣmaṇa, Jānakī, victory to Māruti!": a salutation to Rāma, Lakṣmaṇa, and Sītā, Jānakī being another name of Sītā, meaning 'daughter of Janaka,' and a prayer for Māruti's victory. Māruti is Hanumān, the monkey devotee of Rāma, Lakṣmaṇa, and Sītā, who as a child had taken the orange form of the rising sun actually to be an orange, and leapt towards it to eat it, with disastrous consequences to his chin. ('Hanumān' means 'of burnt chin').

The paurāṇika reflected that that tell-tale mark on the face of Māruti, i.e. evolving humanity, recalling a mercifully abandoned raid on the Sun of spiritual realization regarded as external to the Self, could not be excelled as a warning to the species against regarding environing nature as external to its good, and therefore as harmlessly denudable and limitlessly devourable. A prayer for victory to Hanumān was a prayer for victory to the existentially self-realizing, ethically and ecologically sensitive adventure of life and civilization on earth.

The paurāṇika also realized for the first time — such was the revelatory power of Ananyā's discourse at dawn — that in view of the metaphysical groundedness of ecological and ethical sensitivity in the very name 'Hanumān,' it was only appropriate that ahiṃsā's chief contemporary authority, present at the assembly, should bear Māruti's valorous name — 'Mahāvīra.' The storyteller would have dearly loved to have shared these insights with the assembly, but Ananyā's own story was veering towards its decisive phases, and so the paurāṇika sat down resignedly, and all eyes, including his, urged her to continue. The widening and diversifying chorus of bird-chatter which had been set off by formal sunrise also mysteriously quietened down, and Ananyā resumed her narrative of flight and fear and freedom:

> Runners of my tribe always invoke the name of Māruti, the flying devotee of Rāma and Sītā, to bear them quickly to their destination: so did I. 'Servant of Sītā, victorious Mahāvīra, bear me swiftly and safely to Jānakī's feet, a poor slave begs of you in the name of the divine trinity' I said in my heart and ran and fell and got up and ran only to fall again and again into ditches that night illumined by a full moon too dangerously brightly for a fleeing, thieving, slave.

Ananyā was tired and sat down in the kneeling position, untied her hair in an unfurling gesture even as the story of her tryst with destiny was unfurling. The paurāṇika was transported into samādhi at the synchronicity of his and Ananyā's remembrance of Māruti.

Viśvapriyā, Lopāmudrā, and Parantapa made unbreakable kṣatriya vows in their hearts to journey as soon as possible to Sītā's Kitchen to atone for āryan abuse of aboriginality.

Ananyā was in full flow again:

> And soon enough the hunt started with trumpeting elephants, deafening drums, barking hounds and screaming stalkers. I now ran in no fixed direction, but in several directions as fast and as far as possible from the shifting source of hunting noises, assisted by native training but much more by destiny in my desperate flight from and on behalf of humanity! After what must have been several hours of running, punishingly excessive even for an ādivāsī woman's heart, I collapsed in a thicket of bushes not far from here, thinking only of Sītā and allowed the power of her unconsciousness to pull me into the heart of deep, defiant, sleep. And I had a dream. I am surprised I am alive to share it with you, and that I wasn't eaten up by hungry beasts or vultures while I slept. The Divine Mother had mercy upon me.
>
> I could still be dreaming that dream, because it foretold events leading up to this assembly and prepared me for it and envisioned the distant future too.

I dreamt that I was in a small boat, which was being rowed across a turbulent river—yes, on a night of the full moon—by an aged ascetic with a luminous face and sad eyes, but the boat did not seem to be moving at all. My mother, long deceased, was also in the boat, sitting between the ascetic and myself and seemed to want desperately to make me understand what the holy man was saying, for he was indeed talking to me without my being able to follow his speech at all. It wasn't that he was speaking a language unknown to me, for it was in our own forest dialect that he was speaking: it is *what* he was saying that I couldn't for the life of me understand despite my mother's mediatory efforts. Both of them looked sad as a result and despite vigorous rowing, our boat remained unmoved, although it was being dangerously rocked by the raging river. Then it was that my mother revealed that my name had been given to me by our boatman, and as I then looked at his sad eyes, everything he was saying began to make sense to me; and our boat slipped into slow but indubitable motion.

I gathered that the old man was a descendant of ādivāsī king Guha himself, friend and boatman extraordinary to Rāma, Sītā and Lakṣmaṇa; and that like all his ancestors he had sought to keep alive the intimate link between aboriginality and advaita symbolized by the embrace of kinship between Rāma and Guha immortalized in the Rāmāyaṇa. That embrace, he explained, was not only a seal of political partnership between ādivāsīs and āryans, but of the deeper identity between the mystical polytheism of aboriginal consciousness and the upaniṣadic revelation and realization of singular self-consciousness. I have been able to grasp the essence of some of these terms used during this colloquium because of this dream instruction which I was privileged to receive from a descendant of one who was privileged to receive such instruction from Rāma himself.

Maṇḍūka,[34] for that was the ādivāsī advaitin ascetic's name (i.e. a frog who reins in all dualistic propensities in samādhi) had sad eyes because aboriginality and advaita had long ceased to be in a metaphysical relationship of intimate embrace; and because this had led to an ossification of advaita and a massive dark age of forgetfulness of upaniṣadic teaching as such had descended on this land, marginalizing aboriginal communities and mind-bogglingly sub-dividing āryan communities. Those who refused thus to be segregated and stratified were declared untouchables and cast out of the pale of social and spiritual concern.

Maṇḍūka prophesied that nihilism of an extreme kind, of the kind represented by Masters Ajita and Makkhali in our own age, would also gain adherents in all future ages all over the world, because without the intimate embrace of aboriginality and advaita in life and thought, there was little hope of life and thought embracing one another; and that as a consequence, individual and collective egoism would grow unchecked and the collapse of life and civilization on earth would remain for a long time a terrifying possibility.

But as our little boat continued its slow journey shorewards, Maṇḍūka looked compassionately at my mother, and then at me, and held out hope. 'Do not fail to honor Sītā's Kitchen,' he said, 'because at a time of great crisis in the remote future, humanity may discover its significance as the nourishing power of aboriginal advaita and advaitin aboriginality and live in civilization and realization. Indeed a rediscovery of paurāṇika wisdom in general may close the gap between life and thought, aboriginality and advaita. But until then, the human species and indeed all life will have to bear harsh burdens of division and destruction, until the embrace of Guha and Rāma becomes visible and intelligible and irresistible again.'

I was now in my dream beginning more passively and sleepily to listen to Maṇḍūka's words, not actively interpreting them, so I shall report the rest of my dream in the listening mode. I heard Maṇḍūka say the following things rowingly, sleep-inducingly, liberatingly: 'In your own time, Ananyā, in your own part of Bhāratavarṣa, on the shore beyond this dream river of doubt, there have arrived two sages, Buddha and Mahāvīra, of whom you have heard, but the full significance of whose emergence in Bhāratīya and world history will be adequately understood only in the distant future. It will be understood by the discerning that the traditions inaugurated by the Buddha and Mahāvīra have the capacity indefinitely to fill the vacuum created in Indian civilization by the disengagement of its aboriginal and advaitin visions and forms of life and consciousness from one another. But it will only very gradually be understood by a sufficient number of people that the Buddha's greatest gift to humanity is his realization and restatement of the non-dualist truth of the upaniṣadic tradition without recourse to the scriptual authority and vocabulary of that tradition: a simulanteous vindication of independence and inheritance.

'And even more gradually will it be understood that Mahāvīra's call to ahiṃsā or non-violence is a rediscovery and renewal of aboriginality's ancient manifesto of self-restraint: a tribute of ethics to ecology. Self-realization and self-restraint—the heart of advaita and aboriginality—would thus, through the advent of the Buddha and Mahāvīra, become available to all humanity, Indian or non-Indian, Vedic or non-Vedic, aboriginal or non-aboriginal, at a time of grave crisis in the not too remote future. Don't ask me if this novel reunion of advaita and aboriginality will suffice to save life and civilization on earth from annihilation. I do not know. It might.

'Ananyā, your very name means that which is not other, that which is self, and you, an ādivāsī woman, are going to play an unexpected but fateful part in the slow process of recovery of spiritual self-confidence by the human species which is commencing right now. At this very moment, under a generous banyan tree glistening in the light of the full moon, not far from the shore we have almost reached, the Buddha is instructing arrogant kṣatriya men and women in self-inquiry without even mentioning the Upaniṣadic or the Vedic traditions in which these beautiful people have been most inadequately schooled. You will join them and the Buddha and Mahāvīra soon in a great forest battle of wits with nihilism's pioneering representatives, Ajita Keśakambalin and Makkhali Gośāla, whom you know, but of whose power of unsettling self-confidence and upsetting self-realization you have little experience yet.

'All the life of the forest, its rich self-restraint, its aboriginal advaita, will be regnant in you and by its grace you will find the words and the wisdom you will need. I do not know how the battle will really go. But it will inaugurate possibilities that will fertilize centuries from now. And it will set you free. You must experience this momentous stirring of self-knowledge yourself. There, there is the shore!'

Maṇḍūka had stopped speaking. I awoke from my listening sleep in my dream. My mother's warm hands which had held mine in wordless communion while Maṇḍūka was speaking slipped away. I opened my eyes and found I was alone in the boat which was racing toward a rock on the shore. Maṇḍūka and Mother had disappeared. I closed my eyes in fear again and then came the crash, the boat had hit hard rock. Too frightened to scream, I opened my eyes and found myself in the thicket of bushes where I had collapsed; the dream had vanished.

X

The ornaments were safe in their girdle round my waist. I was breathing and alive. But how was I to get to Ayodhyā? I hadn't even crossed the forest. Maṇḍūka had asked me not to slacken in my remembrance of Sītā's Kitchen; but he hadn't said a word about how I was to get there with my precious cargo of offerings. I smiled wearily at this thought, for Maṇḍūka had been but a dream figure; and while I can now, in retrospect, appreciate the prophetic power of the dream discourse, there in the bushes crouching in fear and hungry and thirsty on that night of my flight I was not thinking of the future of life and civilization on earth, but of my own chances of surviving the night. I must have slept for a couple of hours, because the moon was no longer in the center of the night sky but had moved considerably away leftwards and the pattern of stars too had changed significantly. But all hunting noises had ceased. The silence of the night seemed quite conventional, broken only by routine hootings of owls and insomniac flutterings of tired wings.

But there was one unusual phenomenon, quite unthreatening, but most remarkable, which guided my attention and altered my situation from a position of abject horizontality to bipedality and even humanity, a process which continues. Waves of cricket-noise emanating from the top of a distant banyan that I could dimly discern above the bushes in front of me kept caressing me comically and compassionately, returning to the tree top and coming back, and returning again, most unlike anything I have heard or felt in the quiet of a forest night in all my life. I felt certain that only a power of limitless love could transform the strident cacophony of cricket-sound into humorous, undulating, music; and that it must be the same power, in league with the same banyan tree, that was responsible for the dissolution of the fury of the hunt. I had to respond to the call of the tree, come what may.

Graduating first to quadrupedality, I grazed silently forward to the farthest ring of high bushes between me and the banyan; and then raising myself as high as I could on my knees I peered through some gaps in a bush and what I saw took my breath away. The great tree was not more than a hundred yards ahead of me, a stage, with undulating cricket-song of compassionate unorthodoxy as background music, and the scene of the play? A ring of torch-flames surrounding the central trunk, servants and lords and ladies now discernible or imaginable with the aid of inference; further away backstage several horses and one elephant in reverential attendance.

So this is what Maṇḍūka had said was happening here and now on the shore of my dream river: arrogant aristocracy was being instructed in self-inquiry by the Buddha (whom I could not see, nor imagine) without any scriptural presuppositions. Was this the commencement of the process of recovery of spiritual self-confidence by the human species of which Maṇḍūka had spoken, and what could be the role he said I was going to play in this process? But that was all a dream, I had to remind myself, how could I be sure of what was going on under the musical tree?

Setting aside the claims of doubt and certainty, and the clamor of thirst and hunger, I remained transfixed for several minutes by the sheer beauty of the banyan stage softly floodlit by angular moonlight, and the mystery of the ritual of lights being performed on it by quiescent arrogance and set to avant-garde cricket-sounds of humorously humbling, non-violent, power, the like of which had not been heard before even in this forest of surprises. Then the arc of lights became a procession which moved slowly towards the horses, transformed itself quickly into ạ disciplined cavalry force, and rode slowly away. Defying its mahout's prodding, the lone elephant stayed for a moment, trumpeted a prolonged poignant note of salutation to the tall thin figure in a flowing gown whom I could now clearly see under the tree, and then thundered along behind the horses.

For several minutes I tried to fix my gaze more sharply on the standing figure around whom the banyan seemed to unfurl like a halo, although I could also see an actual circle of light around his head. Maybe that was only a ring of fireflies, but that is also special, because I noticed last night that fireflies chose to form such rings only around the Buddha's and Mahāvīra's heads.

Viśvapriyā and Lopāmudrā and Parantapa simultaneously recalled that unknown to her, Ananyā's head had also been ringed by fireflies, just before dawn broke and Parantapa wound up his disquisition and when she was pouring water for the Tathāgata to drink; telepathy caused them to catch one another's eye and they smiled in shared acknowledgment of the mysterious participation of nature in the drama of the ongoing inquiry. The sun, tossed further up by the quickening day, was red like the 'bindī' on the forehead of a bride symbolizing the third eye, i.e. the eye of self-knowledge, with which alone bride and bridegroom can see their non-duality. It occurred to Parantapa that the red sun with which the sky is anointed at dawn is the eye, symbolically, of insight, with which alone the non-duality of emptiness and ātman, nirvāṇa and mokṣa, can be seen. Ananyā was also lost in contemplation of the deep red and warm blue of dawn, but with some urgency quickly returned to her narrative again:

Only two weeks ago, right here, near where Master Ajita is sitting (Ananyā was kind, for Ajita was asleep again, and Makkhali was plucking lice from Ajita's head of matted hair and his scrubby beard) is where I saw him standing through gaps in that row of wild bushes a hundred yards or so behind where he and Lord Mahāvīra are now seated (so they were, feeding some early rising peacocks with grain from their palms). It was deep night and not dawn, but the Tathāgata was sharply silhouetted by moonlight.

Occult light or fireflies, cricket-sound or gandharva music, what is the difference? He was being celebrated by reality and I had to join in that celebration. I crawled through the bush and stood under the vast emptiness of the night sky and folded my hands in homage. He raised his right hand in abhaya mudrā, offering me freedom from fear. I had no doubt that he was the Buddha, no doubt that Maṇḍūka's dream discourse was becoming reality; and that the abhaya offered to me by the Tathāgata included freedom from the fear that had kept me running for hours like a hunted animal, the fear that I would be caught and summarily killed by my owners for the offense of attempted escape and theft. But more mysteriously and fundamentally, the sage was liberating me from duality, the root of all fear, by the simple act of walking slowly towards me, holding what looked like a pitcher of water between his hands, even as I walked towards him with bated breath and folded hands and sailors' legs (remember I had been in a boat adrift for countless dream hours).

The waves of cricket music had now acquired an ecstatic pulsatoriness and teasing slowness, and bore the following words of the Tathāgata even before he spoke and I, an unlettered ādivāsī slave, was enabled to receive them with understanding: 'Our walking towards each other abridges the distance of duality and highlights the singularity of selfhood. The circumambient sky which envelopes us and all things is self's image of itself, not as a thing among other things, but as limitless inclusiveness. Material earth, which upholds us and all life, is self's image of itself as a sheer massive givenness, its rolling roundness symbolizing the essential self-restraint of the intricate causality of its invisible parts and processes. Forest life, even in its frenzy of mutual devouring, is self's image of vibrant self-consciousness as a free giving and receiving of itself in manifestation; a process which is therefore as patient as it is passionate, unsentimentally but massively ecological.

'The Sun of Vedic and Upaniṣadic self-realization has for a long time now been deeply obscured by scholastic and sociological insensitivity. The Tathāgata was born, attained enlightenment, and will die on a night of the full moon, demonstrating and dramatizing the possibility of illumined mind attaining to self-realization independently of scriptural authority, although not in contradiction to it. The limitlessness of the night sky's emptiness unfurled by the full moon is a reminder of the boundless light of the noonday sun, as is nirvāṇa of mokṣa, śūnyatā of self.

'You will soon also meet Lord Mahāvīra, the Tīrthaṃkara, who was born, attained enlightenment, and will die on a moonless night. He precedes the Tathāgata, demonstrating and dramatizing the possibility of radical non-violent conduct, ahiṃsā in all details of human life, independently of aboriginal authority, but not in contradiction to it. When neither sun nor moon illumine our path, we must tread the earth very gently, causing no avoidable hurt to any creature, thus bringing deliberately and self-consciously to human life the ecological sensitivity massively embedded in the overall scheme of non-human life: and such sensitivity is self-realization, it reflects at its deepest level the conviction that in hunting any creature avoidably, we deny ourselves, not only because we are all *creatures*, but because we *are* all creatures. The disengagement in recent centuries of āryan and aboriginal sensibilities from one another has necessitated the rediscovery of aboriginal advaita by the Tīrthaṃkara in ahiṃsā.'

"The disengagement of aboriginality and advaita from one another!" The very words used by Maṇḍūka. Was I still dreaming and in my dream being rowed across a turbulent river by Guha's descendent? I was not, and yet it was even more dreamlike to see the shore itself, in the form of the Tathāgata, move towards me, as I moved towards him across a clearing in the forest as treacherous as a river in spate for an escaped slave.

The Buddha's words flowed on in authoritative and compassionate vibrations of cricket sound: 'Enslaved and compromised though it is increasingly, aboriginal humanity still matchlessly images self's beginninglessness in its dateless cohabitation with all non-human forms of life on earth. A regenerate modernity would cease to be a past-denying and a future-destroying aberration if it became a trustee of contemporaneity, self's intimate image of itself as ever-presentness, timelessness, unfading freshness; thus acquiring the status not only of civilization but also of recurrent realization.' There was a pause now, forest music brought forth no more words.

I had been walking with my eyes half-closed and receiving and storing away in my brain the mysteriously transmitted words of the Lord as a scriptural message specially meant for safekeeping by aboriginal humanity through me, when the thought of safekeeping shook me into a tormenting realization of my own betrayal of trust. The ornaments concealed round my waist had also been given to me for safekeeping. Yes, in the name of Maṇḍūka and my mother, I can swear that it was disgust with humanity's violation of nature's trust that had made me run away with them, and not only my desire for freedom and the pain of being left out of aristocracy's closed circle of companionship. And I had resolved to risk life itself to make an offering of these ornaments on behalf of all humanity, and not only on my own or aboriginality's behalf, to the Divine Mother at the site of her Kitchen in Ayodhyā.

And yet when aboriginal rage and devotional enthusiasm were ambushed by moral self-questioning, like a proud twelve-horned deer by a tiger lurking in the bush, I knew I was not atoning for but adding to humanity's crimes of betrayal of trust and I collapsed and lay prostrate on the ground once again, beaten down this time not by exhaustion but remorse. I had widened, not narrowed, the distance between aboriginality and advaita. The duality of sage and slave was not any more being dissolved by walking, for I looked up with tear-filled eyes to find that the Buddha's feet—he was so near, yet so far—were stationary.

Cricket sound was now breathlessly palpitating and its music anxious and accusatory. As the vibrations swarmed like bees into my brain, I poured into them the following lamentation, loud but soundless, hoping that reverse transmission would communicate my cry for help to the Tathāgata:

'Lord,' I said in the emptiness of my heart, 'I know you stand there with a pitcher of water to slake the thirst which is killing me, but I thirst for forgiveness more. I, a slave, have betrayed the trust reposed in me by my owners and run away with their ornaments, which I had hoped to offer as a gesture of atonement for humanity's thieving betrayal of nature's trust to Sītā the Divine Mother at her holy shrine in Ayodhyā. But I can see by the grace of the stern shadow of your form cast by the moon between us that this offering would be polluted because the ornaments have been stolen, even more seriously because in running away with them I have been a betrayer of trust: betrayal cannot atone for betrayal.

'The ornaments are no doubt further polluted by the fact that they are tied in folds of cloth round my waist, in intimate embrace with fallen flesh. But this is not why I cannot offer them to Sītā or to You, because I am willing right now to offer my flesh to the purificatory hunger of scavenging birds and animals, the untouchables of the forest; or to the cleansing fire of the funeral pyre. The jewels will be licked clean by vultures and jackals and spat out, like bones, or fired to an even keener radiance by the funeral pyre, and should be acceptable as a purified aboriginal gift to Sītā, the advaitin alchemy of the earth, or to the Tathāgata, the advaitin accommodatingness of the sky.

'The reason I cannot offer them to Sītā or to the Tathāgata is because, unlike my bones, the jewels are not mine. At least at the level of appearance, they belong to my owners, and must be returned to them. But fear and pride prevent me from doing so. Fear of being killed by those who are also thieves in their own way, and who will certainly not restore me to freedom even if they do not kill me. My ādivāsī pride seeks a less humiliating way out of my dilemma. And by Your and Sītā's and my mother's preceptor Maṇḍūka's grace, I think I now see what that way out is.

'I beseech you, āryan light of aboriginality, to tear from the hem of your holy garment a portion of saffron cloth and let me gather the stolen jewelry into a pouch that I will make from it with its own threads and a thorn for a needle. Thus purified and secured in a saffron womb, symbolizing renunciation's creativity, I shall leave the ornaments with you. I saw my lords and their ladies talking with you a while ago from my hiding place behind those bushes. No doubt they will come again looking for me. Lord of the full moon, when they come, give them the pouch and ask them to make an offering of it along with all its contents to the Divine Mother. Tell them too that I am on my way to Ayodhyā myself, to make an offering of my life to Sītā and that they need not look for me anywhere. They may not listen to you, of course, and try and hunt me down. But that will be a welcome death, on my way to the Divine Kitchen, a hastening of salvation.

'The jewelry inside the saffron pouch will be visible to whoever opens it, but at the first touch of human hands it will turn into a mixture of ashes and flowers. I say this with whatever power of prophetic authority that still attaches to my silenced, sullied, aboriginal voice. Tathāgata, forgive me. Take the future away from me along with the burden of theft, but don't ask me to go back in time to slavery. Grant my prayer. I seek refuge in you.'

Having unburdened myself of this prayer and prophecy, my head felt completely emptied of all transmitting vibrations as I lay sprawled and exhausted on the ground. I seemed to have arrived on yet another shore in my dream journey through reality. This shore was two bare feet hardened by tireless walking as my probing hands realized and quickly retreated and returned to clasp them and there were only ceaseless tears of arrival and absolution now. The night air was still; all mediatory noise had stopped.

XI

'Ananyā,' he said in his own voice, 'I have been waiting for you:' I had never known such acceptance. 'Tathāgata, I am waiting for death,' I said. 'You have allowed your ego to die quite a bit, and that is sufficient dying for now. You are thirsty, my child. Get up and let me pour you down some water to drink,' he said. A ceaseless stream of cool water poured on from the pitcher held by the Buddha, enough to quench my thirst and wash away the tiredness of not only several hours of wandering in the forest, but of several lives of wandering in the world. He insisted that I dry myself with the long upper part of his robe thrown over his shoulder; mother and father was he to me in his caring compassion. Then we sat down face to face in the middle of that clearing [the clearing, Parantapa reflected, of causal self-restraint which makes communication possible and non-dual], and witnessed by a retreating moon who seemed glad to have found a worthy substitute after a long night-shift of labor, the Buddha gently spoke as follows:

'The self-restrained, ecstatic, duality-dissolving sound of cricket music has mediated communication between us. Your prayer is granted. Your persecutors were indeed here not long ago and we talked under the banyan. They were a crowd and came on horses and an elephant was in attendance too, a hunt party. They asked me if I had seen in flight or spoken to a young slave girl: name Ananyā, attractive, ādivāsī, and avaricious, who had run off with many of their precious ornaments entrusted to her care by them. Punishment for an escaped slave who is also guilty of theft is summary execution, they informed me. Could I help? they asked. Help in the hunt for her with information, collaboration, for a consideration?

'Cricket sound does not only mediate communication between receptive persons separated by great distances in a forest; it also intricately weaves and casts a witnessing and protective net of waves and vibrations in and around the forest as a whole, especially on a night of the full moon. Catching distress signals like fish, this net transmits them instantly to anyone in the forest who is unblemishedly awake like the full moon. Thus it was that I had learned of the distress of the men and women whose jewelry you had run off with, and of your poignant plight as a hunted slave. I saw that the forest had become a stage for a drama whose meaning was deeply connected with the fate of the earth; and that some of its crucial movements would unfold under the banyan where I sat in meditative watchfulness, over the next fortnight.

'I reminded the couples of noble birth that "Ananyā" meant "no other," "self," the true trustee of all wealth of manifestation, that of which all manifestation was an image; the true "extra," without a peer, unlike their escaped slave who deserved a companion; that which can never escape, but from which they were escaping in acquisitive self-forgetfulness; a truly noble thing, although not a thing among other things, unlike corruptible flesh and evanescent power and wealth; that which those of noble birth should seek; indeed that which confers nobility on whoever seeks it; seek the self, I said, not your slave.

'Certainly theft is reprehensible, I told them; and that if I were to encounter their escaped slave, I would try and persuade her to return the ornaments to their lawful owners; but that if she were to seek refuge in me, in the truth of emptiness and self, nirvāṇa and mokṣa, I would not be able to deliver her over to them; that they would have to seize and kill me before laying their hands upon her; that they would be welcome to do so as I would offer no resistance, although the deed would recoil not only on them but arbitrarily and chaotically on all life on earth, as every evil deed does; that they were welcome to a fuller discussion of all these questions a week later, during the afternoon under the same tree; but until then, or later, there was no question of my assisting them in hunting down the ādivāsī girl for any consideration whatever; that I would be quite happy to assist them in hunting down the far more elusive, although ever-present, reality, self, which bears all the treasures of all the worlds; and of which the castelessly inclusive sky above us and around us and among us, bearing the full moon's seal of perfection, was the perfect image; and of which ecological and ethical sensitivity, and the fearless pursuit of truth, were the finest flowerings in nature and culture.

'I noticed that especially two young women, who looked like sisters, and a young man, were keen to debate the whole question of self and slavery and civilization with me and with one another, and showed signs of remorse on their faces for the intensity and the scale of the hunting operation launched against you. (This reference to them made Viśvapriyā, Lopāmudrā and Parantapa glow with pride this time at being included in the unfolding of destiny.)

'I also heard some grumbling remarks from some others about the inadequate quality of Vedic and Vedāntic instruction and debate in traditional schools and royal courts these days. This I knew to be the case from my days in Kapilavastu and was therefore able to feel some compassion for the wayward hunters. Also gravely whispered by background figures was the warning that no fundamental change in the philosophical orientation of contemporary free-thinking aristocracy was conceivable without a confrontation in debate with the Nihilist Masters Ajita Keśakambalin and Makkhali Gośāla, whose authority was acknowledged by avant-garde thinkers in high places in many kingdoms and republics in the land.

'Anyway, the party disappeared on their mounts, but not before promising to send a representative group to parley with me again a week from now on the whole range of questions that had arisen around my offer of help in spiritual inquiry, and my refusal to help in the hunt for you. The lone elephant in tow bellowed a poignant request for inclusion in the deliberations at least as a subject-matter of substance; and that was the end of that encounter with nobility in need of something noble.

'I cannot abandon those who take refuge in me, no more than self can abandon any self-image of itself or emptiness any evanescent entity open to it, or life any creature who lets live.'

I had been listening with folded hands and closed eyes to the Tathāgata's narrative of destiny. There was a pause, and I knew what that meant. This time too, as before when there had been a pause in his musically mediated words, I was being situated in self's autonomy, in the freedom of conscience and consciousness. Without opening my eyes, and without any instruction or request from him, I released the three cloth-girdles of betrayed trust from my waist and with eyes still closed, poured out their contents on to the ground without remainder, and opened my eyes cast downwards. The entire cargo of gold, diamond, silver and jade had fallen on a stretch of saffron cloth that had in anticipation, and in foreknowledge of my visit, been spread out on the ground between us, a blessed piece of the hem of my Lord's holy garment.

Together, sage and slave, aboriginality and advaita, a man and a woman, detached several strong lengths of string from the cloth, and with readily available thorns from nearby shrubs as needles, stitched in no time a strong pouch of the kind forest healers use for carrying precious herbs; and poured all the jewelry into it and securely tied it at the mouth with saffron strings knotted in the shape of the symbol 'ॐ' which my mother had received from Maṇḍūka as a mark and mantra of timeless antiquity and limitless encompassingness. And the pouch found refuge in folds of saffron close to the golden flesh of the Enlightened One.

'Ananyā,' he said, 'You have sought refuge in me. You and I are now one in the trusteeship of self's insistent self-imaging, emptiness' ardent art-work, life's mission of ministration. When your erstwhile owners come here in a week's time, I want you to be here and we will together declare our bonded subjection in self-realization to self, emptiness, and life; and to nothing else. You will be set free immediately when, ritually, with your formal consent, this pouch — symbolizing, as you have rightly perceived, the wealth of renunciation not the renunciation of wealth, the creativity of emptiness not the emptiness of creativity—will be handed over by me to the two sisters and the young man who I know will be here, with the request—not a command—that it be offered as a gesture of atonement on humanity's behalf to the Divine Mother at Her Kitchen Shrine in Ayodhyā, and the aboriginal prophecy about the fate of its contents should they be touched by human hands. Your request will be their resolve two weeks from now.

'I can foresee the distinct possibility of the sisters and the young man asking you to accompany them to Ayodhyā; and I would urge you to accept their invitation and assume the responsibility of a priestess of aboriginality and advaita and make the atoning offer to Sītā of this symbolic saffron womb of renunciation pregnant with the manifold illumination of civilization and realization.

'The chanting of AUM, the sacred symbol and sound handed down by the ascetic Maṇḍūka to your mother, is a sufficient invocation of sacredness. The "A" sound in 'AUM' represents the sacredness of non-living material reality's structures and networks of self-restrained causality and the inbuilt and practiced ecological restraint, respectively, of non-human life and aboriginal humanity. The "U" sound in AUM represents the ceaselessly vigilant ethical and ecological sensitivity of a regenerate modernity in its creative celebration of contemporaneity. The "M" sound in AUM is representative of the silence and restfulness of trust, which is not the predictive knowledge, e.g., that life and civilization on earth have an inexhaustible future; but the unshakable confidence that they are well-grounded in ultimate felicity and are not an aberration of existence in the midst of a devouring, annihilating, nothingness. Equivalently, we could say that the "A," "U," and "M" sounds in AUM represent, respectively: day and wakefulness, evening and dream, night and sleep—their massive givenness, fragile creativity, and restful power.

'In the chanting, breathing, of AUM, its parts are simultaneously traversed and transcended and breathlessly held together in timeless mokṣa, nirvāṇa, and deathless, birthless, eternal life: in Sītā's Kitchen. Events tonight in the forest have set in motion a process which will attain final consummation two weeks from now, on a night of the full moon again; a consummation which will be like seed in time's fertile ground and with blessed anonymity put forth throughout vast stretches of future time on earth shoots and buds and flowers and even fruitions of trust in reality: perfections of realization more important than predictions of limitless longevity for life and what passes for civilization on earth.

'Ananyā,' said the Buddha—how self-realizing it is simply to be addressed by him!—'you must now sleep under the banyan, and I must remain awake in vigilance by your side and be receptive to distress signals through the few hours of night that remain: and we must await future events with the patience of Guha and Sītā.' As soon as he had spoken these words, cricket music started all over again. Victorious without vanity, sad without despair. I was lulled by it to sleep, gathered into the dreamless womb of trust.

Morning came. I ate some fruits—figs and a 'Sītā-fruit'—which the Buddha had gathered for me before I awoke, but not he: he only ate once a day in the afternoon, like a lion, partaking of what his disciples brought from their rounds of begging in the villages around the forest. He asked me to go to my own village, to share with my family and clansfolk the truth I had been witness to, and to return to the banyan sanctuary at the end of the week in the afternoon for the anticipated rituals of liberation and confession of faith, restoration of property and transference of trust. And he asked me not to fail to have a darśana of Lord Mahāvīra.

'Ananyā, do not forget that you are not in self-realization in bondage to the Tathāgata. You are free to do what you think is right.' These were his last words as I prostrated before him, walked some distance away from him without turning my back towards him, then ran like the wind for miles over familiar forest territory without fear and fatigue until I was home again, the cluster of huts at the edge of the forest which was our compromised, diminishing, but still proud aboriginal kingdom: battered but blessed trustee of the embrace in antiquity, and timelessly, of Guha and Rāma.

XII

The week passed quickly enough. It was marked by incredulous fearful reactions to my story in my village. Reprisal was feared, mass enslavement, and worse. No such thing occurred. Even touts who lure aboriginal flesh to the cities for a paltry consideration failed to show up, and there was much remembrance of Maṇḍūka and artists cast new images of Guha and Rāma and Lakṣmaṇa and Sītā for ritual worship, and storytellers kept young and old awake through long nights. Singing and dancing were frenzied and melancholic, and alcoholic, as usual; but strangely, like the last refrains of cricket music I heard in the Tathāgata's presence under the banyan, they were without vanity or despair.

(How alike collectivity and individuality can be, both self-images of self-consciousness! Thus reflected Parantapa.)

Ananyā continued:

As the Tathāgata had wished and foreseen, I had a darśana of Lord Mahāvīra. The Tīrthaṃkara came himself with a few bhikṣus to beg in our village! Mahāvīra, Hanumān's namesake, heroic both: the former in his devotion to the non-duality of sky and earth, Rāma and Sītā, and the latter in his insistence on ahiṃsā, on the inseparability of living and letting live. With several companions I prostrated before the Tīrthaṃkara and his party and received his blessing of abhaya, wordlessly.

Shortly afterwards I saw Masters Ajita and Makkhali at the weekly bazaar in another village not far from ours. They were not strangers to me. They were frequent guests during feasts and discussions in many of the noble houses where I had served in various capacities; and Master Ajita had on some of those occasions spoken embarrassingly loudly, and I think falsely, about my 'wonderfully cynical lips,' to use his charming expression, as embodying the skepticism of the half-moon regarding the intentions of the night-sky, something astronomically salacious like that being his meaning, I fear; but I had also discerned in his demeanor a much unloved heart for which I felt compassion.

On seeing me at the bazaar, the two came charging down towards me; and while Master Makkhali continuously but silently wagged a reprimanding finger at me, Master Ajita asked me to convey to the Tathāgata the information that he was expected to attend with or without his followers a forest colloquium that they were convening on the date of the next night of the full moon, starting mid-afternoon, under the very same banyan tree where, to quote Master Ajita's words, 'Gotama had sought to undermine aristocratic adoration of absurdity, and annihilationism's avant-garde authority.' Vardhamāna, Master Ajita added, meaning Lord Mahāvīra, had been already informed. I was asked to come too, to help arrest 'absconding aboriginality's advaitin assimilation,' to quote him again. The two then stuck out their betel-juice-reddened tongues at me, turned around, and walked off in the direction of a stall where nothing was being sold; and started selling it, in invisible packages of varying size.

On the night before the fateful day of reckoning and restoration when I was to confront my hunters in the presence of the Buddha, I had a terrifying dream which could easily have launched me on a suicidal journey to the river Sarayū and vindicated absurdism, had the dream not transformed itself into the most perfect image of faith and hope that I can conceive of.

I dreamt that I was dressed as a bride and standing under this great tree, facing its main trunk, mercifully sheltered by its high-rising and far-flung scaffolding and vast foliage from lashing rain on a moonless night continuously stabbed by lightning and reviled by thunder: a perfect image of the security of aboriginal life against the furies of fate and the hustlings of history. Then, in the dream-light of an unbelievably enduring stretch of sheet lightning, I saw the sheltering tree transform itself. Its rooted and long swinging branches became Mother Kālī's trampling legs and arms bearing chillingly splendiferous weapons of destruction. The tree's foliage her cascading black matted hair, thunder her mocking laughter. Forked lightning revealed two familiar figures seated on either side of an ugly stump, for that is what the tree's central trunk had become: Masters Ajita and Makkhali, with red tongues sticking out and eyes daring me to look up and behold Kālī's face. 'The face of the reality of death dissolving into nothingness the appearance of life and existence, the sacraments of love and freedom.' I heard these menacing words mouthed by howling winds of doubt.

Remembering my mother's Rāmāyaṇa explication that each time Rāvaṇa looked at her lustfully, Sītā assumed her Kālī form, and that this is what had deterred Rāvaṇa from violating Sītā during her captivity in Laṅkā, I disbelieved those doubting words borne by demonic winds, and with a terrorized but trusting heart, slowly moved my head upwards with only half opened eyes which closed the moment they encountered the first garland of heads.

'Gracious Sītā', I said, 'I know those garlands of heads only represent your refusal to disown responsibility for the occurrence of death in the ecology of life; they are meant, like all the rest of your Kālī form, the form of Time, to frighten not faith but only diabolical depredatoriness into submission to the discipline of self-restraint. But blessed mother, I do not yet have the courage to behold with the same trust your blood-curdling eyes and tongue. You have tested me severely already; now I am going to test you. If you are my beloved Sītā, divine nourisher of all creatures and structures of existence, as soon as I throw my head high up and open my eyes, let me behold your benign Lakṣmī face of distracting beauty and immeasurable benevolence.' And with a shout of 'He Sītā!' I did just that.

What did I behold? Through the foliage of this witnessing tree, now restored to its sacred botanical splendor, a radiant sun in a luminous sky streaming down its rays of blessings upon ādivāsī, absconding, advaitin, Ananyā; and on either side of the restored backbone of blossoming life, the seated forms of Lord Mahāvīra and Lord Buddha in deep meditation. Directly in front of the trunk on the ground was a rolling board covered with offerings of fallen leaves and flowers and ashes and a rolling pin resting across it, the deity forms worshipped at the site of Sītā's Kitchen in Ayodhyā and in our villages too: symbols of creativity and humble apparatus of bread-making. I lack the language and learning necessary to interpret this scene, but that was the face of Lakṣmī, beauty unexcellable.

Ananyā paused for several seconds here, holding the blessed vision before her closed eyes. The paurāṇika whispered the following paraphrase of the revelation to a novitiate sitting next to him: "Terror transformed into trust. The terror of nothingness transformed into the splendor of the sun of self-realization one with the limitless expanse of emptiness illumined by it. The apparent heartless violence exhibited by non-human life seen in ecological perspective as the stately tree of interdependent life. The apparently mindless fury of non-living material reality seen as highlighting, by contrast, the much more dramatic self-restraint of its causal processes and formations beautifully imaged by the restrained sphericality of the earth supporting the tree of life. Hedonistic contemporary civilization's distrust of ascetic sagehood corrected by the fact that the tree of life is flanked in the vision by guardians of renunciation, who nourish it with tears of compassion and fence it with the discipline of self-restraint, without which the tree cannot attain to fruitfulness.

"And at the foot of the tree, linking matter and life and emptiness, are the rolling board and pin, aboriginality's invocation of the sacred forms of female and male genitalia in its worship of Sītā's nourishing power. These forms in their combination of enveloping creativity and penetrative linearity represent the self-restrained shudder of love's ecstasy, not atavistic abandon as misperceived by contemporary civilization. Appropriately, the offerings on the rolling board are leaves, flowers and ashes stressing the complementarity of biological life and death—of what is and what is not—in the eternal life of self-realization."

Ananyā resumed her narrative:

> The events of the following day were more like a dream than this dream which filled the vacuum of my heart with the fullness of reality, but which I could not at all have understood or even dreamt without the instruction and inspiration I had received from the Tathāgata, and in an earlier dream, from Maṇḍūka. But the ritual of liberation that I am about to recount can only be understood in the light of something very important which happened on the previous day.

XIII

> An old woman sage of our village to whom I had poured out my story, Śabarī is her name, was sorely troubled about the status in aboriginal law of my likely imminent release from bondage. Slavery was recognized in our system of law pertaining to women as a form of forced marriage of slave to master or masters, and only another marriage along with formal liberation could annul it.
>
> But I was not prepared to rush into a marriage. So much had happened to me in the last few days which I needed to absorb into my mind and body and soul, a process which in the nature of things had to be slow and thorough; rushing into marriage was incompatible with this obligation which experience

had placed upon me. I was in a cruel dilemma. I wanted to be set free by the Tathāgata from bondage to otherness, but I respected my own aboriginal traditions too deeply to flout them.

Śabarī, whose wisdom and celibacy had won her a high jurisprudential and spiritual status in our community, decided to confront the Buddha with this dilemma and set off alone to parley with him under the great tree. She had left at dawn and came back in the evening, managing to spend two whole hours with the Tathāgata.

Śabarī came beaming toothlessly into my aunt's hut, which I shared, and announced that ādivāsī law would not be infringed by my release from slavery because the Buddha had explained that the same ritual which would secure my release from servitude would also enact my marriage to all-encompassing emptiness, limitless self-realization: and that it could well happen that at some point in the future emptiness and self may manifest as a flesh and blood bridegroom, marriage to whom would not be a third marriage for me, but only an endorsement of my marriage to sky and self.

The legist also informed us that Prince Parantapa and Princesses Viśvapriyā and Lopāmudrā had also been present when she visited the Buddha. They had come to invite him to a great debate that Masters Ajita and Makkhali had planned for next week in the forest at the same venue (Didn't I know!). They showed appreciation of the Tathāgata's resolution of the dilemma created for the liberation of a slave by ādivāsī law, but were nervous about the outcome of the debate next week between nihilist power and spiritual authority and appeared anxious not to engage in a preliminary discussion of the issues with the Buddha out of respect for the sentiments of Masters Ajita and Makkhali.

The Tathāgata, on his part, made it clear to them that he could part with the saffron pouch containing their jewelry only in my presence the following afternoon. (Śabarī had taken a basket of wild berries as an offering of lunch for the Buddha, but unfortunately almost every other berry was bitter. Nervously, but politely, the Prince and the Princesses declined to eat them. The two sages polished them off. Each would give the other a sweet berry after tasting it, reserving the bitter ones for themselves!)

The fateful day dawned. An early swim in the cool stream which flows between the edge of the forest and our village washed away the exhaustion of the dream-filled night that had just ended; and then Śabarī and my aunt dressed me up as a bride in my mother's nuptial robe, a single red-bordered length of coarse white cloth which had been spun and woven by a sister of Śabarī's. Marigolds in my hair and a garland of them and leaves around my neck were my only ornaments, and on my round forehead suggestive of a rolling board, Śabarī formed with ash the figure of a rolling pin: aboriginal wedding make-up. And she then played on a gnarled flute a dramatic set of three descending notes — *sa-pa-sa* (the last, fifth, and first note of the octave) — three times, lingering quiveringly on the concluding *sa* each time; an aboriginal ritual sound of inauguration. And then the two of us set off immediately for the sacred venue, walking slowly because of Śabarī's arthritis and age. In four hours — at high noon — we sighted the banyan's green dome shining in strong sunlight; its hanging, interlocking, branches looking like floral decorations on a royal pavilion. We could not yet see the King; but the sight of stationary horses and dismounted guards at some distance from the structure enabled us to infer that we had been preceded by noble personages. Soon we were admitted into the royal court by the King of Kings himself.

At an auspicious moment chosen by Śabarī (the moment of confluence of two quivering ellipses of reflections of the banyan's anatomy on the ground which had been silently advancing towards one another), the Tathāgata asked me to stand directly against the trunk of the tree, with Śabarī facing me at a distance of ten feet. He himself stood six feet away from me on my right, holding the saffron pouch in the hollow of his cupped hands; and six feet on my left stood Prince Parantapa and Princesses Viśvapriyā and Lopāmudrā in a small arc, with several of their companions behind them. A small crowd of inquisitive deer and peacocks had gathered behind the Tathāgata and a whole platoon of pigeons fluttered off the higher regions of the tree and flew above and around it in eccentric ecstatic formations.

The Tathāgata looked at Śabarī, took her wide grin as permission to begin the proceedings, and spoke as follows: 'Śabarī, as an ādivāsī woman jurist and sage, you are the chief witness of the ceremony about to commence, even as aboriginal humanity has been the chief witness of the dateless sport of self on earth. Ananyā, standing against the trunk of this tree, is a slave bonded for life to the families of Prince Parantapa, Princesses Viśvapriyā and Lopāmudrā, who stand in front of me, and others. She is guilty of theft and attempted escape. The saffron pouch in my hands contains the ornaments that had been entrusted to Ananyā by her owners for safekeeping a week ago in this very forest and with which she ran away. She surrendered the ornaments to me, and also sought refuge in me on the night of her escape, shortly after her pursuers had met me right here under this tree.

'The law of the land requires that I should hand over the ornaments to their owners, and so I shall in a minute. But the law of my being prevents me from handing Ananyā over to them. She cannot be apprehended or punished for her offense now without spiritual injustice. I can, and readily, offer myself as a substitute. I discussed this matter with Prince Parantapa and Princesses Viśvapriyā and Lopāmudrā yesterday, but they are unwilling to commit or allow to be committed by others the sin of enslaving and punishing—by death, as the law requires—a sādhu whose dharma it is to protect those who take refuge in him: and this is a noble decision on their part which will bring blessings to them and arbitrarily also to many others, such being the reckless benevolence which springs from noble thoughts and deeds.

'Ananyā wanted to make an offering of the ornaments at Sītā's Kitchen Shrine in Ayodhyā as a gesture of atonement for the sins of our species; and I would urge Prince Parantapa and others seriously to consider doing so themselves, although neither Ananyā nor I can demand this of them. But I must remind them of Ananyā's prophecy, made with all the invocatory power of aboriginality's accumulated austerities, that if they are touched by human hands, the ornaments would instantly turn into ashes and flowers — traditional ādivāsī offerings to Sītā not only in Ayodhyā but in the humblest of village shrines. Untouched and offered to Sītā, they may save the earth from catastrophe in some future age of extreme crisis.'

Then, following the Tathāgata's instructions, I walked round the sacred trunk three times slowly, as he chanted 'AUM' —Maṇḍūka's mantra gift to my mother—in perfect synchronicity with my circumambulation. Śabarī then played on her flute, now in ascending order, the set of notes — *sa-pa-sa* (the first, fifth, and last note of the octave)—three times, lingering breathlessly on the first *'sa'* each time: an aboriginal ritual sound of accomplishment.

'Ananyā,' the Buddha declared, 'you are now restored to your timeless marriage to self and emptiness, mokṣa and nirvāṇa; aboriginality and advaita are reunited in you once again. This is the most ancient of unions, of Rāma and Sītā, of the vast inclusiveness of the sky and the vibrant self-realization of the earth. Your spouse the sky may manifest in this or another life as a flesh and blood human bridegroom, and your marriage to such a man would be a reiteration and not a violation of aboriginality's marriage to advaita. You are now free to dissolve your bondage to your owners—regarded as a forced marriage in ādivāsī law, according to Śabarī—by asking me formally to return this pouch to any one of the three owners of yours standing in front of me, in exchange for your freedom which they have agreed to restore to you by tearing up right here in our presence the palm leaf (which they were good enough to show me before you came) record bearing your mother's thumb-impression signing away your freedom for life.

'Tathāgata,' I cried, 'Give the pouch to Princess Lopāmudrā, I beg of you, for her name celebrates the restoration of a lost ring. The ring of my marriage to the sky was lost, and you have restored it to me.'

The Tathāgata gently walked up to Princess Lopāmudrā, whose eyes were closed, and placed the pouch in her trembling hands. He raised his right hand in abhaya mudrā, offering peace and fearlessness to her and Princess Viśvapriyā and Prince Parantapa, who took out from the fold of his upper garment a single large leaf of palm and slowly and gravely tore it to shreds, casting the bits away to be swept along with other fallen leaves on the ground by a sudden gust of wind which stormed the amphitheater, frightening away the deer and the peacocks.

The Buddha became very grave now, also Śabarī, alert like animals to distant dangers. The wind was getting stronger and raising dust along our route back home; the pigeon platoon returned flutteringly to its resting perches: the Prince and Princesses and their companions did a quick and half obeisance to the Buddha and walked briskly away to their waiting, neighing, mounts and rode away. Śabarī and I prostrated ourselves before the saffron king. I noticed the torn hem of his gown and was blinded with tears.

Celibate flautist and freed slave trekked back to their aboriginal village speechlessly, Śabarī's flute breaking the silence from time to time with an asthmatic rendering of an aboriginal ritual sound of liberation: the two-note *sa-sa* testimony of self's unmediated realization of itself, the self-same first and last note of the octave.

It was only late in the evening in my aunt's hut, as I massaged her aching arthritic limbs, that Śabarī explained to me that my release from slavery and simultaneous marriage to the sky consecrated by the Buddha symbolized ego's release from ignorance and simultaneous entry into mokṣa or nirvāṇa. She reminded me that my marriage to emptiness was not yet consummated, that self-consciousness in me had not yet become self-realization. I realized I had to journey far for that consummation. Outwardly, symbolizing an inward trail, to Sītā's Kitchen, with or without Prince Parantapa and Princesses Viśvapriyā and Lopāmudrā. I had wanted to throw myself into the river Sarayū in Ayodhyā. What I was now called upon to do was to offer my ego of injured innocence to Sītā for alchemical transformation into the uninjurability of self and pour my pride even of aboriginal antiquity into the ever-fresh stream of her ceaseless timeless grace. That is the only way not only of battling but also of curing the arrogance of ignorance, old or new.

XIV

I must wind up my testimony now. I am grateful to Masters Ajita and Makkhali for being like thorns without which the pleasure of running barefoot in the forest would only be a half-pleasure, without instruction in caution and incentive to innovation. And thorns have their uses too (Ananyā caught the Buddha's eye as she spoke the words)! Their invitation to me to participate in this assembly is more important than their intimidation, which alone after all can test the heart[35] of compassion adequately.

If the sky were a denouncing nothingness, the earth a cauldron of causal fury, survival an unrestrained slaughter, and society unmitigated slavery, the tree of life on earth would not bear such fruits as the Buddha, Mahāvīra, Maṇḍūka and Śabarī (she would have been present here if she hadn't been doubled up with arthritic misery) and other sages known and unknown who fear and frighten no one. It is worth nourishing this tree with speech and silence, life and death, music and mourning, revolution and realization, so that it may bear such fruits always. Even if a cosmic storm were to blow this tree of life away, its Kālī form would deter that violence from violating its integrity, even as Rāvaṇa was deterred from violating Sītā as he bore her away to Laṅkā in his flying chariot. The fruits of the tree would scatter seeds of self-realization all over the universe and sooner or later these would sprout into new earths, forests, banyans, lives, sages, civilizations.

'The sport of self,' to use a phrase of the Tathāgata, is ceaseless. Spoilsport ego may distort the play, obscure the light of self-realization more deeply than death does. But even in deepest obscurity, I am convinced, fireflies of illumination would guide ego back to the truth of self and emptiness which it caricatures and conceals.

Besides, all storms of destructiveness and all forms of self-obscuration can be neutralized by faith in Sītā's Kitchen, in the creative laboratory which the earth is in its spinning self-realization and in the all-inclusive Rāma-embrace of the sky's emptiness, and through obedience to their ethical and ecological commandments. It is because of such faith and obedience that aboriginality is datelessly old, not because of a mere longing for longevity.

Not being able to find appropriate concluding words, Ananyā paused, drinking some water from a small pitcher which Viśvapriyā had considerately placed near her.

Parantapa formulated a thesis in his mind.

"Anxiety and annihilation are distinctive features of modern civilization. All anxiety is rooted in the false belief that apparent otherness is real otherness. And annihilationism is absolute anger against appearance thus misconstrued, seeking ultimate fulfillment through an attempted realization of total insensibility via a holocaust destructive of all life on earth. Annihilationist anxiety is the extremest form of dualism: and it can only be cured by the purest form of non-duality, advaita, which sees appearance as the self-imaging of self-realized self-consciousness, and not as otherness demanding to be indulged or intimidated. Ethical and ecological sensitivity is an ultimate artistic responsibility, self's responsibility of adequate self-imaging in idioms of independence and interdependence."

Parantapa's thoughts were interrupted as Ananyā resumed her concluding remarks:

Destiny has manifested between two successive nights of the full moon and beyond a drama which began with inequity, both āryan and ādivāsī, and matured into testimony, again both āryan and ādivāsī. In between have figured the unclassifiably unique grace of Tathāgata and Tīrthaṃkara, Buddha and Mahāvīra, and the interrogation of self-confidence by the similarly matchless nihilism of Masters Ajita and Makkhali.

Let this drama conclude with an initiation of inquiry, the inquiry recommended by the Tathāgata to those who thought they had been robbed and betrayed: the asking of the question 'Who am I?'

Is there another, a not-I, who can rob me or whom I can rob, who can betray or be betrayed by me? Was I bound, and am I only now free? Was I born and will I die? There is certainly the appearance of others, and of otherness; of robbers and betrayers, of enslavement and liberation, birth and death. But is such appearance reality? It is certainly not unreality, in the sense of unencounterable impossibility. Is not the appearance of others and otherness more like the surreal malleability of clay with which images can be made both of Rāma and Sītā, and of Rāvaṇa and Śūrpaṇakhā[36]? Of the Yādava dance of self-destruction and of eternal Rāsa Līlā?

Am I not then Sītā who unfurls the sky as self's roofless, wall-less, theater of compassionate inclusion of all images of itself in a whirl of ecstatic interdependence which excludes and enslaves no one? Am I not then Sītā who in graceful self-restraint fashions the earth as self's image of its own rounded perfection, a trustee mother of all her children at play, and not a betraying stealer of their toys? Who am I?

Ananyā had concluded her testimony and fallen into silent meditation on her knees, palms resting on them like trembling leaves, breathing indrawn and eyes closed. She was soon in a waking dream. In a boat once again with Princesses Viśvapriyā and Lopāmudrā as companions and Prince Parantapa as boatman vigorously rowing their boat across the river Sarayū to Ayodhyā's shore. A saffron pouch rested in her lap. There was flute music wafting across the waters from Ayodhyā, bearing the aboriginal ritual sound of inauguration — *sa-pa-sa, sa-pa-sa, sa-pa-sa* — in units of three haunting repetitions with which Śabarī had launched Ananyā's journey to freedom.[37] Her advaitin journey on behalf of humanity had begun. She rolled down exhausted on the ground, horizontal once again.

The sun was high and hot now. Viśvapriyā and Lopāmudrā gently lifted Ananyā to her feet, to bipedality, and when she opened her eyes and also saw Prince Parantapa standing in front of her, her sense of the difference between waking and dreaming was further challenged. It was totally undermined when, turning right round, she saw, among her other ādivāsī companions, old Śabarī playing the familiar snatch of *sa-pa-sa* notes on her flute. The sage had felt better early that morning and at once started her journey to the great forest debate, arriving limpingly but fatefully punctually during the final minutes of Ananyā's call to self-inquiry, which brought forth her flute number of inauguration. "Who am I?" asked Śabarī mischievously and mysteriously as Ananyā hugged and kissed her, forcing the octogenarian to sit down. Overwhelmed by surreality, born-again ādivāsī and advaitin Ananyā sobbed away with her head in Śabarī's lap.

XV

For the paurāṇika and his two novitiate disciples, ādivāsī sage Śabarī was none other than she of Rāmāyaṇa fame[38] whose pretasted berries had been partaken of by Śrī Rāma. They came and prostrated before Śabarī in a small arc. "We know who you are!", "We know who you are!", they said with lumps of humbled learning in their throats. Śabarī covered her eyes with her right hand partly out of modesty, partly because the sun was hurting her eyes; and partly because she wasn't able to believe her eyes; and with her left hand she continued to caress Ananyā's head and face in her lap, all the while making those chewing motions with her mouth which toothless sages of embarrassing antiquity resort to as a substitute for unforthcoming, unnecessary, speech.

Behind Śabarī and Ananyā stood in another small arc Lopāmudrā, Parantapa and Viśvapriyā, bowing low in obeisance to the Buddha and Mahāvīra who stood next to each other at the other end of the forum directly opposite the aristocratic threesome, offering abhaya with raised right hands to all, but with a specificity of attention to the scene of special promise which confronted them: Paurāṇika wisdom prostrating before ageless aboriginality nursing its own new-born spirit of timelessness, guarded by aristocracy's awakened conscience bowing before advaita's new-born spirit of Tathāgata compassion and Tīrthaṃkara ahiṃsā, the whole stage bearing this consummatory formation of self-images in the sport of self now signatured by the light of a resplendent sun of self-realization filtering through the tree of life. A scene for the Gods. Cause for āsuric jealousy.

For some time now, Ajita and Makkhali had awakened from a long spell of sleep and registered their protest against daylight by tying black bands round their eyes. This did not, however, deter Ajita from playing dice with himself by the side of the tree trunk made memorable by testimony. He played his right hand against his left hand continuously and without cheating, but his blindfoldedness wordlessly implied that he was not interested in knowing the outcome of a fair struggle between left and right; or that such a struggle was unwitnessable because unreal; or that over a sufficient period of time, even a fair struggle between left and right, despair and hope, was bound to end in hope's defeat and that he was willing to wait indefinitely to behold the inevitable ultimate outcome of this struggle. Anyway, there he was, vigorously demonstrating the hope of despair against hope. It was impossible not to notice Ajita's act. The paurāṇika was riveted by it. "Would the Pāṇḍavas have prevailed against the Kauravas without Kṛṣṇa's rules-transcending assistance?" he wondered troubledly. It occurred to him that future Bhīṣmas and Droṇācāryas and Kṛpācāryas would be well advised to help prevent a Kurukṣetra war and not risk it, because Kṛṣṇa may not be around next time to outmaneuver the Kauravas; and future Yādavas may destroy more than themselves.

Makkhali too was undeterred by blindfolding and climbed higher and higher up the banyan gymnasium, vigorously swinging upside down on each trapeze-worthy branch before transcending it. Ananyā was washing the Tathāgata's feet with water and the salt of her tears, but many of her ādivāsī companions and also Śabarī were gripped by Makkhali's nihilist gymnastics. Even Parantapa, Viśvapriyā, and Lopāmudrā, who were busy planning an early pilgrimage on foot to Sītā's Kitchen led by Ananyā, were obliged to call off their confabulations by the weird Master's treetop wizardry. What was he implying?

> 'Could he be saying,' thought Parantapa aloud after a few moments of meditation, 'that only the blind imagine, i.e. those who are blinded by the lure of life, that upward evolution along the tree of life towards so-called spiritual realization can correct the essential upsidedownness of the nature of things, their design for disaster? That even from the highest branches of being and becoming in evolution, one is only hung upside down, a small slip away from a hurtling fall into oblivion? And that no amount of civilizational acrobatics can prevent this programmed humiliation of height? Could this be his mute message? Are the Buddha and Mahāvīra on the edge of annihilation? How absurd!' But Parantapa's voice conveyed a worrying note of bravado to himself and others.
>
> Śabarī came to the rescue. 'Even caricature teaches the truth it caricatures,' she said, the compulsive chewing motions

of her mouth and jaw suggestive of a maternal gift of premasticated wisdom for easier digestion by younger generations.

'Whatever be his communicative intention,' Śabarī explained, 'Master Makkhali's blindfolded daredevilry is brilliantly indicative of humanity's blindness to existential, ecological, and ethical imperatives in its greed for higher and higher levels of hedonistic consumption; and the dangerousness of such blindness. Also, my perceptive Prince Parantapa, whatever be the wizard's intention, his circus act under the banyan's canopy can teach discerning children of all ages to avoid vertigo in spiritual progress by choosing to be blind to the altitudes scaled along the way to the summit which is egolessness. Master Makkhali is mistaken, however, if he thinks his brinkmanship proves that even the Buddha and Mahāvīra are poised for annihilation. Their ego is already annihilated in their plunge into fathomless compassion and ahiṃsā.'

Śabarī's jaw continued to execute chewing motions long after her table-turning reading of Makkhali's menacing meaning had comforted the entire assembly which was now on its feet, collectively watching in awed silence this crowning circus act of the colloquium, wondering when the appropriate moment would arrive which would signal its conclusion and permission to everyone to go home after nearly eighteen hours of exhilarating but exhausting deliberations.

The moment came soon enough. By design, although it looked like an accident, Makkhali failed by inches to grasp the highest visible branch of the banyan and began his tumble down, somersaulting all the way with legs rolled up and held tight between his arms, breaking his fall on softer branches and foliage and landed in seconds on his well-padded bottom next to Ajita on the right side of the trunk.

The fall was ominously followed by a significant quaking of the earth, sending everyone into a shaking dance of laughter and screams, with the exception of a few sages who also shook but without laughing or screaming; compassionately, amusedly, reassuringly.

The big tree shook and winged creatures shot off from it into the sky in wide arcs of alternative security, and a variety of other forest cries of distress were also heard. Also, unbelievably, flat on the ground though she was on her back, Śabarī produced a primevally loud version of the aboriginal flute call of radical transformation — *sa-sa, sa-sa, sa-sa* — which Ananyā had described in her testimony, stilling the tremors and the cries of distress and reversing the flight of birds from the tree to the sky and restoring humanity to proper bipedality from the indignity of comic and anxious shaking. The Buddha and Mahāvīra, unfelled though they were by the quake, still wore huge smiles of ill-concealed amusement.

Assisted by Ananyā, Śabarī also painfully stood up, her victorious asthmatic panting reassuring especially Parantapa that while the earth suffered much from nihilist assaults, it still responded to the pacifying magic of spiritual transformation.

XVI

Ajita and Makkhali had also stood up, removing their blindfolds. During the interminable seconds of the earthquake, the duo had been busy, shaking like others though they were, but with an exaggeration of enjoyment at what they regarded as a consummatory vindication of themselves. Ajita had frenziedly detached a large patch of densely-knitted hair from the hem of the gown-like blanket of hair that he wore, and Makkhali had gathered all their dice (cut from human as well as non-human bones, it seems) into the hairy surface, folded it and tied it up severely with several knots into a menacing bundle: a fist clenched with the confidence that probability favored catastrophe. Ananyā, who had rushed to Śabarī's aid when the tremors started, had watched this nihilist imitation of saffron grace and guessed the purpose behind it.

Ignoring the standing assembly which was dying to be dismissed, Ajita and Makkhali now proceeded to play ball with the hairy bundle, tossing it back and forth into each other's hands, Makkhali all the while whistling *sa-sa, sa-sa, sa-sa,* in mocking imitation of Śabarī, and not without the hope that this piece of blasphemy might trigger a convulsive quake. Large-hearted earth didn't oblige.

Then with the bundle in his left hand, his right hand caressing it, Ajita fixed his gaze on Ananyā alternatingly ferociously and pleadingly, and in a like mixture of tone of voice, spoke as follows:

> The half-moon, like your former mouth, will mock at an incomplete offering to Sītā, the offering only of saffron-seduced atonement. Take to Ayodhyā this fist of hair also, defiant disbelief in divinity, pure power of probability; and let the dice it protects contend in the bowels of the earth with the jewels of faith

> you want to sow there, side by side. Two sets of seeds, let us see what Sītā's alchemy makes of them. You see your jewels blossoming into a new tree of life, don't you, Parantapa, Viśvapriyā, and Lopāmudrā, you skeptics of little faith! I see nihilism's dice sprouting into a series of mushroom clouds of climactic catastrophe!

"Ananyā!" cried Ajita uncontrollably plaintively now: "Do not forget to offer honest hair along with sanctimonious saffron to the Divine Mother!" Stepping forward, he placed the bag of dice in Ananyā's hands, enclosing them with his own. He was overcome for a whole minute with an emotion of the heart which the pride of his mind finally stifled, making him quickly step back to his station of authority.

"Ananyā!", he thundered now, "And if you touch these dice with your hands, they will turn into jewels and precious, priceless, ornaments!" Having found concluding words of appropriate temptation, Ajita resorted to mocking laughter and gestured wildly with his raised arms, signaling the end of the great forest symposium. Makkhali clapped continuously and self-congratulatorily and also as though he was scattering away a horde of intrusive pigeons. The spirits of some of their followers who had felt dejected during the conference now revived, and they lustily joined their leaders in the gesticulations and clapping of dispersal and dismissal. Then they all ran in quite different directions for a long time, in ritual non-conformity, before assembling together again on the horizon way behind the banyan, and disappeared over it.

XVII

Some of the kṣatriya friends and relatives of Parantapa, Viśvapriyā, and Lopāmudrā, who had been ardent admirers and patrons of Ajita and Makkhali, but who had experienced painful disillusionment with them during the course of the colloquium, were much relieved by Ajita's pleading command to Ananyā to make a formal offering at Sītā's shrine of both jewelry and dice. This enabled them psychologically to continue to admire the original, unpredictable, prowess of Ajita's mind, and also endorse without reservations Parantapa's, Viśvapriyā's, and Lopāmudrā's resolve to take the saffron pouch with its memorable untouchable contents to Ayodhyā under Ananyā's leadership. Thus politically and philosophically reassured, they joined their more unconditionally transformed fellow kṣatriyas and Ananyā in detailed planning of the atoning pilgrimage, and also sought vigorously to persuade the latter of the "fairness" of Ajita's request.

Lopāmudrā, especially, needed persuasion, as she had been deeply shocked by the sly and salacious and slanderous manner in which Ajita had made the request to Ananyā. They took the matter to the Paurāṇika for adjudication. He was in a trance of bhakti and heard Lopāmudrā's disgusted disapproval of Ajita's spanner in the wheels of karma with closed eyes but close attention, and reminded her of Śrī Kṛṣṇa's claim in the *Bhagavadgītā*[39] that the cunning of the gambler was also he, self, Kṛṣṇa himself. He is the contrition of the contrite too, he added commentarially, opening his eyes suddenly and staring self-congratulatorily at Viśvapriyā; and ruled that illumination and ingenuity were both Kṛṣṇa-blessed and appropriate as offerings to Sītā's Mahālakṣmī manifestation in Ayodhyā. Viśvapriyā lowered her eyes and smiled in amused acknowledgment of the suppleness of the Brāhmaṇical mind.

The paurāṇika's ruling was accepted by all, and Ananyā gladly gave Ajita's precious dice in their endearing encasement to the aristocrats for safekeeping. "We won't decamp with them!" they said, and all laughed; but not without nervousness, for they could not deny that like the Rāmāyaṇa and Mahābhārata, an epic fortnight had ended with auspiciousness bedeviled by ambivalence.

Anyway, with the Paṇdita's further encouragement and astrological assistance, felicitous dates and hours of departure for the pilgrimage were fixed. "We'll keep in touch," said Lopāmudrā and Viśvapriyā to Ananyā tearfully, after much mutual hugging watched by Parantapa with empathy but not without envy, for the Prince wanted Lopāmudrā's embraces to be reserved for himself! Simultaneously recriminatory and reassuring glances were shared between them. From a distance, for they were not formal followers, the revolutionary kṣatriya threesome bowed in deep obeisance to the Buddha and Mahavıra, prostrated before the pauraṇika, and proceeded towards waiting horses.

XVIII

With the conclusion of the colloquium, the Buddha's fortnight of vigil under the banyan also ended and he was preparing to proceed with some bhikṣus to nearby villages to beg his afternoon meal, the one meal in twenty-four hours permitted to monks regardless of rank. And Mahāvīra with his followers was planning a visit to a different set of villages for bhikṣā, so as not to be a burden on the villages which the Tathāgata and his party were going to visit. The two sages laughed about this with the ordinariness of saintliness; and then for a full minute, unrecorded by history, they were in deep embrace, shedding streams of tears of compassion for the sufferings of creatures and the distortions and invasions suffered by structures of existence and areas of emptiness in all worlds everywhere.

Overcoming all inhibitions of orthodoxy, the paurāṇika permitted himself the privilege of prostrating before the slowly disentangling embrace of compassion and non-violence, followed by his followers. "I know who you are!", "I know who you are!", he cried in a choked voice which was charged with the power of spiritual discernment. "Whatever your followers and my co-religionists might say, you are Rāma and Lakṣmaṇa, Balarāma and Kṛṣṇa, manifesting in variety the unity of transcendence and immanence, witnessing and participating, gathering and scattering, the rich non-duality of self-realized self-consciousness. I seek your blessings for the paurānika imagination of human spirituality."

Abhaya was transmitted by a pair of raised right hands attached to different bodies, but which were yet a singular reality of reckless generosity, and received by the universe as a whole including the paurāṇika and his followers, Śabarī and Ananyā and their fellow ādivāsīs, and a small mixed group of people who too had not hurried home after the proceedings of the colloquium had been peremptorily concluded by its idiosyncratic convenors.

This latter group included a number of śudras who had sat behind Ananyā and her ādivāsī group at the symposium, some of whom had worked as servants with Ananyā in the same aristocratic households. One of them, an old bearded man, had been in a trance throughout the latter part of the vigil, from the point when Ananyā had begun her discourse. Early in the morning, not long after dawn, he had been blessed with a vision of Sītā—for he too was deeply attached to her Kitchen Shrine—in which he was instructed by her not to desert the conference venue even after everyone had left. He thought with characteristic humility that the Śakti behind the conference no doubt wanted him to clear the litter which had accumulated under the tree. Peels and kernels of fruits, potsherds and sundry other personal things left behind by careless and tired participants anxious to get home after a marathon meeting.

The Buddha and Mahāvīra asked everyone now to get up and return to their homes and loved ones and to their duties. Ananyā and Śabarī and some of the others — ādivāsīs, śudras, Brāhmaṇas, including the paurāṇika, vaiśyas, kṣatriyas — trekked in single file behind the Tathāgata and his followers in the direction of Ananyā's village, at a sharp angle to the right behind the banyan. The rest — also a mixed group — followed Mahāvīra and his followers in like manner at a sharp angle to the left behind the banyan, in the direction of another set of villages quite far from Ananyā's village as the crow flies. Ananyā had asked the bearded śudra, whom she knew, to join the Tathāgata's party; but he had explained, without breathing a word about his vision, that he had austerities to perform, and stayed back.

XIX

The old man watched the two processions flow meanderingly along like streams issuing from a common source until they flowed over the horizon and were gone, like so many movements for a change of consciousness and the circumstances of life which gather around illustrious leaders and disappear from the scene of active life or become distorted after the leaders are gone. But the Buddha's and Mahāvīra's blessings, like Rāma's and Kṛṣṇa's and Sītā's and Rādhā's, are scattered throughout the universe and cannot be nullified by the denials and distortions of history, he thought, as he swept limitless litter aside from the sacred stage under the banyan with an improvised broom of leafy branches, gathering the mess in small heaps for later disposal. Limitless also was the radiance of the sun of self-realization now royally installed high above the tree of life. Awed, the sweeper asked himself the question: "Won't sages like Vasiṣṭha and Viśvāmitra grace this land again and bless the earth with the light of Vedānta? Or will inequity overwhelm illumination?"

When he had completed the labors of his purificatory task, the scavenger priest of the deserted forest temple sat down in meditation at the place he had occupied during the great debate. "Gracious Sītā, bless your lowly servant with a vision of your truth and insight into what leads us astray from it," he prayed. After a measurelessly long spell of immersion in meditation, which was disturbed but not destabilized by cinematic anxiety (the Buddha and Mahāvīra staking and losing all their spiritual wealth in a game of dice against Ajita and Makkhali; Parantapa, Viśvapriyā and Lopāmudrā speeding away in their boat across the Sarayū, deaf to the cries of the drowning Ananyā and Śabarī), the supplicant opened his eyes. It was late afternoon, almost exactly the hour when the colloquium had commenced the previous day. Ignoring all other distractingly beautiful forest sounds and sights, the old man's attention was fixed on a pair of pigeons on a low branch of the banyan, lost in the play of love. "Rāma, Sītā, Kṛṣṇa, Rādhā," he exclaimed in ecstasy, "the non-duality of love, the love of non-duality, that is your truth." And then like a thunderbolt, a hunter's speeding arrow struck and pierced and felled to the ground one of the lovers, leaving the other screaming in inconsolable grief. Ethical and ecological insensitivity had divided in time the timeless non-duality of self-consciousness.

But that is how the Rāmāyaṇa begins. This testimony and narrative must end now, on this note of timeless self-realization and recurrent self-forgetfulness.

NOTES

1. Pitṛ, Guru, and Deva ṛṇa; traditional debts of Hindu piety.
2. *The Gospel of Śrī Rāmakrishna,* translated by Svāmī Nikhilānanda, Śrī Rāmakrishna Math, Madras, 1986. 'The Master and Keshab,' p. 138. I have put the Master's thought in dialogical form, invoking narrative license.
3. While leaving self utterly unharmed, the impact nevertheless destroys the illusion of a separatist self-image ('I am this, as opposed to that'). Non-violence is not impotence. Self-realization, however temporary, is impossible without suffering the shock of a radical disillusionment.

   We suffer this shock, and are ripe for self-realization, each time somebody addresses us. In addressing me you don't refer to me; you mean me, not that I am this, as opposed to that. And addressing is not an act by which you try to cause me to attend to you, but an act of disavowal of attention-attracting causal efficaciousness which constitutes an invitation to me to attend to you of my own free accord. At its deepest level, this invitation is an invitation to me to see you as myself, to regard being conscious of you as self-consciousness.

   Addressing is a recurrent sacrament of everyday life which our recalcitrant 'dehātmabuddhi' (Our 'I am this, as opposed to that' orientation of mind) refuses to receive.
4. A clarification is in order here. Our thoughts, feelings and actions are profoundly and undeniably causally affected by the associative and suggestive power of words, be they words of edifying poetry or manipulative propaganda. But the exercise of this power presupposes the trustworthiness of ordinary communication, which is vouchsafed by the manifest 'non-starter' status of linguistic utterances regarded as instruments inherently capable of causing audiences to believe or do what is propositionally encoded in them. Non-violence is at the heart of human communication, and non-duality *is* the heart of non-violence.
5. *The Life of Svāmī Vivekānanda,* by his Eastern and Western disciples, Advaita Ashram, Calcutta, 1974, 'At Kshir-Bhavani,' p. 598. I have described the event dialogically.
6. "Ijtihād," which means insightful interpretation of religious obligation in changing circumstances, is a sacred injunction of Islamic tradition. See *Ideas and Realities of Islam,* by Seyyed Hossein Nasr, London, George Allen and Unwin, 1966; pp 104, 105, 117, 173.
7. Or cognate Buddhist or Jaina features. There is evidence of a Buddhist and Jaina connection with Ayodhyā, which was also known as Sāketa, from the time of the Buddha and Mahāvīra. Jainism claims an even older connection.

8. A fairly comprehensive account of the Ayodhyā controversy from a variety of contending perspectives can be obtained from the following recent publications:
   (i) *Babri Masjid Ramjanambhumi Controversy,* edited by Asghar Ali Engineer, Ajanta Publications, Delhi, 1990.
   (ii) *The Babri Masjid of Ayodhya,* by R. Nath, The Historical Research Documentation Program, Jaipur, 1990.
   (iii) *Ram Janmabhoomi Vs Babri Masjid,* A Case Study in Hindu-Muslim Conflict, Koenraad Elst, Voice of India, New Delhi, 1990.
   (iv) *Disputed Mosque,* a historical inquiry, by Sushil Srivastava, Vistaar Publication, New Delhi, 1991.
   (v) *Anatomy of a Confrontation:* The Babri Masjid Ramjanmabhumi Issue, Edited by Sarvepalli Gopal, Viking, New Delhi, 1991.

THE DISPUTED SHRINE AT AYODHYA

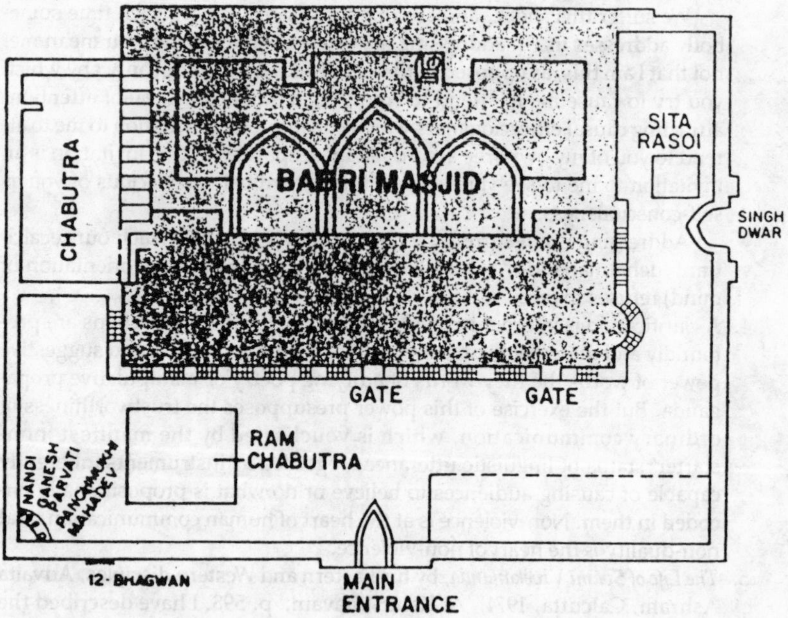

The above is a sketch of the disputed shrine at Ayodhya. The dispute is over the shaded area. The idols are placed under the central dome which was kept locked in the past. Pujaris and other visitors used the gate to the right. Ram Chabutra is a platform under a tree in the outer enclosure. To the right of the main entrance is a tin shed the pujaris use as an office. Sita Ki Rasoi is a small platform to the right. Singhdwar is not in use. The chabutra on the left is raised space. There are several little idols in the outer enclosure where devotees make offerings. The main entrance faces east.

Reproduced, along with the caption, from *Anatomy of a Confrontation*, 'Legal Aspects to the Issue,' p 94, with the permission of S. Gopal and A. G. Noorani.

"Sītā-kī-rasoī" finds frequent mention in Koenraad Elst's study.

Elst refers to a shrine further north of the Bābarī mosque in Ayodhyā (away from the zone of contention) which is also called "Janmasthan Sītā Rasoi" and is regarded by some disputants as marking the real site of Śrī Rāma's birth, as opposed to the site occupied by the mosque. Elst is dismissive of this shrine's claim to birth-place status because his is a strongly relocationist position regarding the mosque. It doesn't occur to him that more than one spot could theologically properly be regarded as marking Rāma's birthplace.

He goes further. He is not even willing or able to allow that more than one site could mark the location of Sītā's Kitchen without any offense to theology or even to royalty. Elst would like to believe that the rival shrine marks the actual site of Sītā's Kitchen, although not of Rāma's birth; and he gives a new identity to the well-known "platform" instantiation of Sītā's Kitchen adjacent to the Bābarī mosque (see diagram above). He calls it "Kauśalyā's Kitchen." This is humorous.

Kauśalyā was Rāma's mother. Presumably Elst thinks that the proximity of a Kauśalyā Kitchen to the Bābarī mosque site would strengthen the claim that that site marks the place where Kauśalyā's palace stood; where Rāma was born; where else? Thus all the way to relocation.

Unfortunately for this argument and aspiration, Hindu domestic life does not distinguish between the kitchens of mother-in-law and daughter-in-law. The mother-in-law in fact hands her kitchen over to her daughter-in-law, to the nourisher of future generations. And Sītā is no ordinary daughter-in-law. She is the Divine Mother. Not Kauśalyā, not in the sacred Ramāyaṇa tradition.

I am not suggesting that the Zone Shrine cannot also be called "Kauśalyā's Kitchen." But Kauśalyā's Kitchen must in epic time metamorphose into Sītā's Kitchen, in deference to rules of domesticity and the demands of divinity. Koenraad Elst is welcome to his relocationist zeal regarding the Bābarī mosque. But he should not encourage the reduction of India's spiritual imagination to literalist aridity, just as he is anxious not to encourage the reduction of articles of faith to historical hypotheses.

9. Fueled as it is by fundamentalism, the demand for the Bābarī mosque's relocation is likely to become more strident and unyielding with the passage of time, and the Indian state may be forced to choose between brutal repression of the relocationists and abject surrender to them. Miracles do occur, however, and a deep-going and extended debate in the country on the moral and spiritual dimensions of the Ayodhyā controversy could win more support for the status quo and the demand for the mosque's relocation may weaken significantly, enabling the state to protect the structure more or less non-coercively.

   But what if this miracle fails to occur? It would then become imperative to defuse the situation without unworthy compromise. I have some thoughts regarding how this could be done, prompted by the idea and reality of Sītā's Kitchen; but the situation in Ayodhyā is still fluid and it might be premature and even counterproductive to spell out these thoughts without consultation with all concerned parties.

Theocratic secessionism in Kashmir and Punjab is also a demand for "relocation": the relocation of Islam in Kashmir and Sikhism in Punjab outside the matrix of Indian sovereignty and civilization, and the concomitant "relocation" of Hindu refugees outside the Kashmir Valley and Punjab, cruel euphemism for the forcible exodus of age-old inhabitants and custodians of the culture of these regions.

Here again, brutal repression of relocationism and abject surrender to it threaten to become the only available, and equally unacceptable, options for the state.

What is needed in Kashmir and Punjab and in the Indian subcontinent as a whole, as elsewhere in the world, is the miracle of a relocation of consciousness within areas of ecological responsibility and imagination, because secessionism and hegemonism in the contemporary world are not political improprieties, merely, but violations of cultural and spiritual ecology.

10. Like the empty tomb of Christ, which suggests "where" he is continuously reborn: in virgin self-consciousness unviolated by ego's shadow. The Christ of the empty tomb is indeed a gardener with a green manifesto for existence. Mary Magdalene had not misidentified him, my Hindu Christology insists.
11. This impulse to annihilation is starkly revealed in Andrei Tarkovsky's film "The Stalker." A stalker of the sacred in a world of fear and greed leads a scientist and a writer ("who want to be paid for every breath they take") to "the zone," a mysterious area like Sītā's Kitchen which has survived nuclear (fundamentalist) devastation. In the small booth at the heart of the zone there is really nothing, except a telephone which could be taken to be the link between bounded and boundless emptiness, self-image and self-realization. The stalker barely succeeds in preventing the scientist and writer (religious bigot and manipulative politician) from destroying the zone with a portable nuclear device (microphone, video cassette).

    Fear and hatred of emptiness and self dominate our age: fear and hatred of space and time, life and environment.
12. *The Rāmāyaṇa of Vālmīki*, translated by Hari Prasad Shastri, Shanti Sadan, London, 1970, Book II, Ayodhyā Kāṇḍa, Chapter 50.
13. *The Adhyātma Rāmāyaṇa* is a fifteenth century work of unknown authorship which seeks systematically to unravel the non-dualist symbolism and significance of the epic, and which accords the status of Self to Sītā, around whom through her māyā-śakti is woven all the drama of the epic.
14. An older composite work whose date is difficult to determine, the *Yogavāsiṣṭha* is a mass of instruction in advaita purported to have been given by the sage Vasiṣṭha to the young prince Rāma. Śrī Ramaṇa referred to it frequently.
15. *The Rāmāyaṇa of Vālmīki*, translated by Hari Prasad Shastri, Book II, Ayodhyā Kāṇḍa, Chapter 52.

16. *The Ramāyaṇa of Vālmīki*, translated by Hari Prasad Shastri, Book I, Bāla Kāṇḍa, chapter 2.
17. See *History and Doctrines of the Ājīvikas*, by A. L. Basham, London, 1951. A formidable sect of ascetic sceptics, the Ājīvikas taught a doctrine of the unalterable sway of destiny and the helplessness of all existence in relation to it. Such a teaching can easily become an invitation to self-destruction and an anticipation of it. It is this possible, annihilationist, form of Ājīvika destinarianism that I have attributed to Ajita Keśakambalin and Makkhali Gośāla in their nihilist incarnation in my narrative. I make this clarification because it is not customary to think of the Ājīvikas as nihilists.

    Unfortunately and unfairly, it is not the Ājīvikas but Buddhists who are called nihilists by Brāhmaṇical polemicists in gross misunderstanding of the Buddhist doctrine of emptiness. Equally unfortunately and unfairly, Advaita is called eternalism by Buddhist polemicists in gross misunderstanding of the upaniṣadic doctrine of self. The fictional debate between Ajita and Makkhali and the Buddha and Mahāvīra and others in this book is liberated from these misunderstandings, and endeavors to represent a cleaner but sharper confrontation between self-confessed annihilationism and absurdism and Indian spirituality. The outcome of such a confrontation cannot but decisively affect the fate of life and civilization on earth; and not only the future of India.
18. Also cited as the "Bhaddavaggiya sahayakānam vatthu". Pālī usage would assign to these phrases the meanings "story of the rich" or "story of the rich young companions." But underlying Saṃskṛta etymology yields the following idiomatic translations of "Bhaddavaggiyavatthu": "Something Noble," or "A thing of class." These are vivid metaphors of self. The English translation of the Pālī text here reproduced is that of Max Müller and his associates, and appears in *The Sacred Books of the East* series, volume XIII, Vinaya Texts, Part I, Mahāvagga, 14: Edited by Max Müller, Oxford, at the Clarendon Press, 1881.
19. What Max Müller and his associates translate as "yourselves" in this utterance, and as "ourselves" in the next, can also be translated as "self"; and the utterances would then read as follows:

    "Now what think you, young men? Which would be better for you, that you should go in search of a woman, or that you should go in search of self?"; and "That, Lord, would be better for us, that we should go in search of self."

    The fear that "self" would be taken to mean an entity of some kind, in disregard of the fundamental "anatta" or "not-self" teaching of the Buddha, seems to have governed the learned translators' choice of the innocuous substitutes "yourselves" and "ourselves." This is unfortunate, because the substitutions obscure the text's bridge-building role between Buddhism and Advaita. The Tathāgata in this text is daring the lost sheep of the upaniṣadic tradition (who are in danger of becoming predatory wolves in that age of metaphysical and moral bankruptcy) to return to its source, self, which is not an entity among entities but non-entitative self-consciousness and self-realization, i.e. emptiness. The rich young companions have not lost their slave-owning status in society, and the Buddha is not asking them to make good a non-existent loss. What they have lost is not status but self, self-realizing self-consciousness; which is what the Tathāgata compassionately asks them to seek.

20. It was a sannyāsin in Vṛndāvana who reminded me that "Bhārata," India's ancient name preserved in its constitution, literally means "obsessed with light" or, quite simply, "enlightened." Not only distinctively Indian traditions of spiritual enlightenment or realization—ādivāsī, Hindu, Buddhist, Jaina, and other, e.g. Sikh—are "Bhāratīya" in this sense, but all mystical traditions of spirituality—Abrahamic and Chinese and African and other; and also all secular traditions of independent inquiry that do not unexaminedly and dualistically align themselves with "reason" as *against* "religion."

    Thus in a constitutive sense, although not by explicit constitutional commitment, India is a Bhāratīya state: a state of enlightenment beyond the dualism of secularism and religion, a trustee consciousness of spiritual and secular traditions of illumination.

    The idea of India as a Hindu state is a distorting diminution of Bhāratīyatā as understood above, as is the idea of Kashmir as an Islamic state or Punjab as a Sikh state. Ideological secularism of the European kind, liberal or Marxist, is equally incongruent with Indian civilization's dateless obsession with the indivisible light of consciousness, even in the midst of darkness. Indian politics must rethink its colonially inherited and communally distorted vocabulary.

21. Reproduced in the Preface. Instead of the harlot I speak of an ādivāsī girl who is alone and not a wife-substitute for the text's lone bachelor.
22. A contribution of modern Indian politics to the art of intimidation, the physical encirclement of a figure of authority by agitators until their demands are conceded.
23. *The Ramāyaṇa of Vālmīki*, translated by Hari Prasad Shastri, Book III, Araṇya Kāṇḍa, Chapter 102.
24. op. cit., Book VII, Uttara Kāṇḍa, Chapters 45–49.
25. op. cit., Book III, Araṇya Kāṇḍa, Chapters 42–45.
26. op. cit., Book VII, Uttara Kāṇḍa, Chapter 97.
27. op. cit., Book VII, Uttara Kāṇḍa, Chapter 110.
28. *Mahābhārata*, condensed by Kamala Subramaniam, Bharatiya Vidya Bhavan, Bombay, 1982, 'After the War,' The Tragedy at Prabhasa, p. 733.
29. *Śrīmad Bhāgavatam*, condensed by Kamala Subramaniam, Bharatiya Vidya Bhavan, Bombay 1979, Chapter 190.
30. *Śrīmad Bhāgavatam:* the authorship of this central scripture of Vaiṣṇava bhakti is attributed to Vyāsa, author of the *Mahābhārata*. The forest groves of Vṛndāvana are the heart of the *Bhāgavatam*, not the battle-fields of Kurukṣetra; harmony, not strife.
31. *Mahābhārata*, condensed by Kamala Subramaniam, Sabhā Parva; Chapters 11, 12, 13, 14.
32. *Śrīmad Bhagavadgītā*, translated by Svāmī Śivānanda, The Divine Life Society, Tehri-Garhwal, 1989, Chapter II, 3.
33. I realize this passage is influenced by the Bob Dylan song "Blowin' in the wind," and how influenced even I was as an oldish Indian student in England in the sixties by "the sixties."

In the present context, two lines from that song are especially worthy of recall: (i) "How many times must a man look up, before he can see the sky?" This line demands to be heard as registering exasperation at those who cussedly refuse to acknowledge pervasive emptiness, i.e. essential Buddhism.

And (ii) "How many times can a man turn his head, and pretend that he just doesn't see?" This line can be heard as registering exasperation at those who stubbornly deny the self-evidence of self-consciousness, essential advaita.

34. The name also of the sage transmitter of the *Māṇḍūkya Upaniṣad*, literally "The Frog's Secret," a canonical scripture of advaita. The Upaniṣad reveals the secret of "AUM": that its three utterance-parts, A, U, and M, represent wakefulness, dream, and sleep; and are traversed and comprehended and transcended by self. AUM is self, its breathless breathing, Śabarī's asthmatic authority in her ādivāsī incarnation in this narrative.

This message of Maṇḍūka rescues from pejorativeness the expressions "frog-hopping" and "frog-in-the-well." Frog-hoppingly, self refuses the fixity of definition, while remaining contentedly sunk in the well-spring of self-consciousness. See *Māṇḍūkya Upaniṣad*, translated by Svāmī Gambhīrānanda, Advaita Ashram, Calcutta, 1979.

35. The heart of compassion cannot be other than the heart on the right side of our chest of which Śrī Ramaṇa spoke, an area of emptiness corresponding anatomically exactly to the fickle pump, the seat of all our anxieties, on the left. This empty heart is where self is situated in the body, Ramaṇa used to emphasize, both playfully (because self is all-pervasive and not in any one place in the body or anywhere else) and seriously (because given the stubbornness of 'dehātmabhāva,' the 'I am this body' orientation of our minds, an area within the body demands to be indicated).

But the heart on the right side of our chest is not only a finite zone of emptiness, like the inner space of the Bābarī mosque or the wider zone of Sītā's kitchen in Ayodhyā; it is continuous with boundless emptiness, as those zones are.

It is the experience of many practitioners of the 'Who am I?' form of meditation taught by Ramaṇa that it is on the right side of the chest, palpably in the area of emptiness which is our spiritual heart, that a current of self-awareness manifests and fructifies as self-realization: in the area as a whole and at every point in it and in every portion of it, not at any one fixed point alone. Rather like the birthplace of Rāma being the kitchen zone as a whole and every portion of it and every point in it, not any one fixed place alone in the zone.

Interestingly, one of the sources of authority cited by Ramaṇa for his doctrine of the empty heart of self-realization (bridge of metaphor and mutuality between advaita and Buddhism) is the *Sītā Upaniṣad* of the Atharva Veda which affirms the reality of Sītā as Brahman, Ground of Being, source of all manifestation. Some scholars regard this upaniṣad as an interpolation. No matter. It must have been illumination which thus waylaid ignorance.

I have inserted this note at this point because, had he been aware of self's heart of emptiness, the paurāṇika would have been stirred to a meditation on it by Ananyā's reference to the heart of compassion; but he would not, as was so often his fate during the symposium, had an opportunity to turn the meditation into an intervention.

See *Talks with Ramaṇa Maharshi*, Sri Ramanasramam, Tiruvannamalai, 1978, for Śrī Ramaṇa's teaching on the heart on the right side; in several places indicated under "heart" in the index.

36. *The Rāmāyaṇa of Vālmīki*, translated by Hari Prasad Shastri, Book III, Araṇya Kāṇḍa, Chapter 17.
37. It was a very similar set of notes, blown with poignant dissonance by an electronic fog-horn, that kept streaming across the bay into my jet-lagging consciousness through the sleepless night of September 30, 1987, which inaugurated a joyous year of teaching for me at the California Institute of Integral Studies in San Francisco.
38. *The Rāmāyaṇa of Vālmīki*, translated by Hari Prasad Shastri, Book III, Araṇya Kāṇḍa, Chapter 74.
39. *Śrīmad Bhagavadgītā*, translated by Svāmī Śivānanda, The Divine Life Society, Tehri-Garhwal, 1989 Chapter 10, 36.

GLOSSARY

abhaya: gift of unanxiousness; liberation from the fear of otherness

abhaya mudrā: symbolic gesture (mudrā) of upraised palm of right hand by which abhaya is given by sages and divinities to all existence; not only to human beings

ādivāsī: aboriginal, "beginningless," human conmmunities; a future non-anthropocentric self-image of humanity as a whole, beyond the pride and shame of history

Advaita: non-duality; classical and continually renewed Indian philosophical and spiritual teaching and testimony of the sole and ultimate reality of self; a saving counter-intuitiveness in an age overwhelmed by the propaganda of dualism, secular as well as religious

Advaita Vedānta: school and system of Advaita philosophy formally constituted by Śrī Śaṁkarācārya in the eighth century A.D. according to modern scholarship; at a much earlier date according to traditional scholarship

ahiṁsā: non-injury or non-violence

araṇya: forest; literally, "that which cannot be battled," metaphor of self

Ārya: supposed racial identity of ancestral Hindus; literally, "noble"

asura: demon

āsuric: demonic

ātmabodha: self-knowledge, self-awareness

Ātman: self; not ego; I; not I as "this" opposed to "that"

Ātman-Brahman: ultimate reality as the identity of Atman, indubitable self, and Brahman, the "Vast": indubitable, intimate, infinity; Godhead

Ātman-Brahman Mary: Christ's mother Mary conceived as Ātman-Brahman

AUM: Hinduism's most sacred symbol and mantra of universal significance. Its utterance-parts A, U, and M represent the waking, dream, and sleep states, encompassing all manifestation. As a complete utterance, AUM is that which manifests and exceeds all manifestation: self

avatāra: divine incarnation

Balarāma: elder brother of Kṛṣṇa who was Rāma's younger brother Lakṣmaṇa during Kṛṣṇa's Rāmāyaṇa incarnation

Bhaddavaggiyavatthu: a canonical Buddhist record of an encounter with the Buddha of a party of young aristocrats; incorporated in the 'Mahāvagga' section of the *Vinayapiṭaka;* a bridge between Advaita and Buddhism which will survive sectarian sniping

Bhagavadgītā, Śrīmad: Mahābhārata dialogue between Kṛṣṇa and Arjuna; for Hindus a scripture of the greatest authority which has deeply influenced the resurgence of Hinduism in modern times

Bhāgavatam, Śrīmad: Vaiṣṇava scripture of unexceedable authority which records the pastimes of Kṛṣṇa's childhood and youth

bhakti: devotion as a path of spiritual realization whose attractiveness reached its zenith in India during medieval times and has not waned.

bhikṣu(s): Buddhist mendicant(s)

Bhīṣma: celibate invincible warrior of advanced age who fought on the side of the Kauravas in the Mahābhārata war despite his affection for the Pāṇdavas; and who instructed the Pāṇdavas in Dharma after their victory in the war

Bose, Subhash Chandra (1897–1945): Charismatic Indian leader who, disagreeing with Gandhi, organized the 'Indian National Army' to liberate India from British rule by force of arms; a fact corrective of the myth that India's struggle for freedom was wholly non-violent. Bose is presumed to have died in an air crash over Japan in 1945

Brahmā: Creator

brahmacārīs: celibate novitiates

brāhmaṇa(s): member(s) of orthodox Hinduism's priestly caste; literally, "seeker(s) of Brahman (the Vast)"

Brancusi, Constantine (1876–1957): Romanian sculptor, Paris-based. His set of 'Bird in Space' and 'Bird' sculptures are suggestive of the miraculous possibility of bombs turning into birds, and other kinds of weaponry into wings. In 1936, the Mahārāja of Indore had tried to commission a set of Brancusi birds for installation in a temple of meditation.

Bṛhadāraṇyaka Upaniṣad: an upaniṣad, i.e. confidential spiritual instruction or secret, of great antiquity and authority; literally, "great forest secret"; metaphor of self an its field of self-images

Buddha: Buddhism's founder; literally, "the awakened one"; unfading spiritual authority and unfailing liberator from unreason

Christ: Christianity's founder and "only son of God." A self-realized sage in the light of Advaita; perhaps Advaita's first martyr. Christ's self-realization in a cultural environment hostile to Advaita is evidence of the universality of self-realization

Churchill, Sir Winston (1874–1965): Britain's Prime Minister and saviour during the Second World War whose hatred of Hitler's racism did not diminish his own racist prejudice against the idea of Indian independence. Dualist moral indignation notoriously keeps falling into such hypocrisy

darśana: visual encounter with a sage or with divinities; also any philosophical system conceived as a coherent vision of reality

dehātmabuddhi: mind-set represented by the thought "I am this body, as opposed to that": source of dualism

dehātmavāda: dehātmabuddhi congealed as a philosophical dogma. Dualism's orthodoxy

Deva ṛṇa: debt to divinity

Dhamma (Pālī), Dharma (Saṁskṛta): universal order which holds all manifestation together integrally, internally; source of the ideal of morality and justice

Dhṛtarāṣtra: blind patriarch of the Mahābhārata, father of the Kauravas; dotingly blind also to the evil designs of his eldest son Duryodhana

Draupadī: common wife of the Pāṇḍava brothers, symbolizing the marriage of unitary mind to all five senses

Droṇācārya: preceptor of both Pāṇḍavas and Kauravas who fought on the side of the Kauravas in the Mahābhārata war

Gandhi, Mohandas Karamchand (1869–1948): political and spiritual leader of India's freedom struggle; pioneering activist explorer of the truth and power of non-violence in society and politics. Post-independence India (not to mention Pakistan) has not been markedly Gandhian in this respect. A disappointment which nevertheless liberates Gandhi from Indian proprietorship

Gāṇḍīva: Arjuna's celestial bow

gheraoing: a modern Indian form of political intimidation; the physical encirclement of a figure of authority by agitators to compel acceptance of their demands

Gośāla, Makkhali: ascetic philosophical freethinker; contemporary of Buddha and Mahāvīra

Gotama: one of the Buddha's pre-enlightenment names

Guha: Rāma's aboriginal companion king in the Rāmāyaṇa; etymologically suggestive of a "cave"; area of mystery and intimacy symbolizing aboriginality and its safe-keeping of Advaita

Guru ṛṇa: debt to preceptors

Hanumān: monkey devotee of Rāma and Sītā; ideal of spiritual devotion and discrimination; literally, "of burnt chin," the name recording a scalding encounter he had as a child with the Sun which he mistook to be an orange; a deep ecological lesson for spiritually evolving humanity

Hindustānī (e.g. music): of Hindustān, northern India; indicative as a concept also of a quality of integration of Hindu and Islamic cultural traditions

Hitler, Adolf (1889–1945): sought world-domination for a supposedly Aryan Germany through mass-murder, especially of Jews, war and conquest and enslavement of other races. Modern exemplifier of the demonic logic and power of 'dehātmavāda' (the "I am this body, as opposed to that" dogma of dualism), which is at the root not only of racism but also of anthropocentric annihilationism; species-facism masquerading as modern civilization

Jaina: a follower of the Jaina religion, Jainism; from "Jina," meaning "victorious"

Jānakī: daughter of King Janaka; Sītā

jñāna: gnosis; spiritual illumination; self-realization

Kālī: Divine Mother; Godhead; destroyer of evil and ignorance

kaivalya: radical self-sufficiency, autonomy; Jaina spiritual ideal

karma (adjective:kārmic): action; ritual; causality of morality and morality of causality; inescapability of moral consequence

Kauravas: the hundred sons of Dhṛtarāṣtra, on evil bent

Kauśalyā: Rāma's mother

Keśakambalin, Ajita: an ascetic philosophical freethinker of great authority; contemporary of Buddha and Mahāvīra

krauñca: curlew birds; the fatal love-play of a pair of them was witnessed by an anguished Vālmīki, causing him to compose the Rāmāyaṇa poem at the behest of Brahmā

Kṛpācārya: another preceptor of Pāṇḍavas and Kauravas who fought on the side of the Kauravas in the Mahābhārata war

Kṛṣṇa, Śrī: Viṣṇu's consummate incarnation; supreme object of spiritual devotion

Kṛṣṇā: another name of Draupadī; literally, "the dark one," like her divine friend Kṛṣṇa

kṣatriya(s): member(s) of orthodox Hinduism's warrior caste

Kurukṣetra: battlefield where the Mahābhārata war was fought; literally, "field of action (Karma)"

Lakṣmaṇa: Rāma's younger brother, ideal of vigilance and loyalty

Lakṣmī: Viṣṇu's consort; incarnate as Rāma's wife Sītā; repository of all wealth of truth

Laṅkā: capital city of Rāvana's kingdom where the demon held Sīta captive

Lenin, Vladimir Ilyich: (1870–1924): architect of the socialist revolution in Russia whose legitimization of manipulativeness and amorality in the practice of political idealism sowed the seeds of the disintegration of the Soviet socialist experiment. Corrective disillusionment for impatient utopianism of all kinds

Lennon, John (1940–1980): British songwriter and pop musician of genius whose search for self-realization was dogged by drug-dependence. Like Gandhi he wore steel-rimmed spectacles and was assassinated

Mahābhārata: epic poem recounting the war between Pāṇdavas and Kauravas and Kṛṣṇa's role in it; context of the Bhagavadgītā

Mahālakṣmī: Lakṣmı not as Viṣṇu's consort, merely; but as the Divine Mother, Atman-Brahman, Godhead; Sītā

Mahāvīra: literally, "great hero"; founder, or one of the founders, of Jainism; Mahavıra inducted the concept of ahiṁsā or non-violence into the consciousness of heroism, like Gandhi in our times

Maṇdukya Upaniṣad: literally, "The Frog's Secret"; a canonical text of Advaita which explicates the meaning of the sacred symbol AUM, and introduces the distinction between the waking, dream and sleep states and the fourth, turīya, "state," self, which includes and exceeds the three states of waking, dream, and sleep. The text is a manifesto of spiritual surrealism

Mārīca: Rāvaṇa's demon kinsman who, disguised as a golden deer, lures Rāma away from Sītā, making it possible for Rāvaṇa to abduct her. The context of the episode is of profound ecological significance

Māruti: another name of Hanumān

mokṣa: release from the bondage of ignorance; self-realization; Advaita's ever-realized goal

muni(s): literally, "the silent one(s)"; spiritually exalted persons whose silence is no less edifying than their speech; a favoured Jaina category of spiritual identification, but not only Jaina

nirvāṇa: Buddha's state of enlightenment, goal of Buddhist spiritual practice; literally, "blowing out" or "extinguishedness" of craving

padmāsana: "lotus" sitting posture symbolizing poise of being and inextricable commitment to spiritual realization

Pāṇdavas: The five brothers, beloved of Kṛṣṇa, who took on the Kaurava horde in the Mahābharata War

Parantapa: another name of Arjuna, meaning "scorcher of foes" as well as "scorcher of otherness"

Pitṛ ṛṇa: debt to ancestors

Rādhā: Kṛṣṇa's beloved milkmaid; esoterically the Divine Mother, Godhead; identical with Sītā

Rāghava: founder of Rāma's dynasty and identity of his clan

Rajagopalachari, Chakravarti (1878 – 1972): Indian statesman and modern reteller of the Rāmāyaṇa and Mahābhārata narratives

rakṣasa: demon

Rāma, Śrī: Viṣṇu's incarnation, immediate predecessor of Kṛṣṇa; object of supreme devotion; the name "Rāma" is a mantra of matchless, integral power, which can in English be read as an acronym for "Reality and Manifestation"

Rāmakṛṣṇa Paramahaṁsa (1836 – 1886): sage of modern India; incarnate unity of diverse paths of spiritual realization. Hope of a future experientially well-grounded global culture of religious tolerance

Ramaṇa Maharṣi (1880 – 1950): sage of modern India; incarnate self-realization; chief authority and exemplar of Advaita in our age. Hope of an undespairing existentialism of future self-consciousness.

Rāmānuja, Śrī: 11th century AD founder of the Indian philosophical system and school of Viśistādvaita or qualified non-dualism which served as a metaphysical foundation for medieval India's bhakti movement.

Rāmāyaṇa: sacred history; epic story, composed as a poem by Vālmiki, of Rāma's victory over Rāvaṇa; the prevention of the appropriation of divine energy (Sītā) by demonic forces (of self-consciousness by ego?)

Rāsa Līlā: mystic-erotic rite of dance performed by Kṛṣṇa and the milkmaids of Braja in the forest groves of Vṛndāvana; metaphor of the passionate ecology of life and existence

Rāvaṇa: demon king of Laṅkā, abductor of Sītā; slain by Rāma (ego-king of the body, abductor of self-consciousness, slain by self-realization?)

Ray, Satyajit: Indian film-maker of great sensitivity who died recently. I have let the present tense of this book's reference to him (p. 27) remain unaltered as a tribute to the enduringness of his art

Śabarī: low-born woman sage with whom Rāma shares a meal of sweet and bitter berries in the Rāmāyaṇa, symbolizing God's participation in our joys and sorrows

Sādhanā: Guru as Truth; Truth as Guru; a self-realized preceptor.

sadguru: spiritual practice

Śakti: Divine Mother; supreme force, energy.

Sāketa: an ancient name of Ayodhyā

sannyāsin: renunciate

Sarayū: sacred river on whose banks stands Ayodhyā, and into which Rāma disappeared at the end of his reign.

Śeṣa: Lakṣmaṇa; residual divinity unexhausted by incarnation, symbolized in mythology by a coiled serpent on whom Viṣṇu rests untroubledly

Sītā: Rāma's wife; esoterically, the Divine Mother, Godhead, Mahālakṣmī

Sītā's Kitchen: minor, barely noticed, shrine in Ayodhā capable of defending the earth against ego

Śiva: God as destroyer of the evil of ignorance; reality as blessedness and auspiciousness

Śrāvastī: ancient Indian city

sukhāsana: unstrained sitting posture in yoga, symbolizing the innateness of spiritual realization

śūdra(s): member(s) of orthodox Hinduism's lowest caste

Śūrpaṇakhā: Rāvana's demon sister disfigured by Lakṣmaṇa when she threatened to devour Sītā (symbol of the unattractiveness inevitably invited by ego, the would-be devourer of self-consciousness?)

śūnyatā: emptiness, not-thingness; Mahāyāna Buddhism's ultimate reality; metaphor of self in the light of Advaita

Tathāgata: literally, "one who has thus come or gone"; the Buddha

Tīrthaṁkara: literally, "ford-maker"; Mahāvīra

upaniṣad: a genre of Vedic texts characterized by confidential spiritual instruction; literally, "sitting near (the teacher, the truth)" or "proximity" or even "intimacy" or "intimation"; an intimation of immortality

upasampadā ordination: initiatory rite of Buddhism

Uruvela: ancient Indian city

Vaiśālī: ancient Indian city

Vaiṣṇava bhakti: way of salvation through devotion and surrender to Viṣṇu or his incarnations such as Rāma and Kṛṣṇa

Vālmīki: composer of the Rāmāyaṇa as an epic poem in Saṁskṛta.

Vārāṇasī: datelessly old holy city of Śiva on the banks of the Gaṅgā, modern benares or Kāśī

Vardhamāna: literally, "ever-growing"; name of Mahāvīra.

Vasiṣṭha: sage preceptor of Rāma

Vedas: Hinduism's most canonical corpus of revelation and realization and knowledge

vicāra: inquiry, especially into self; way of self-realization taught in our age by Srī Ramana Maharsi

Vinayapiṭaka: sacred Buddhist canon of monastic discipline

Viṣṇu: God as sustainer and omnipresent ruler; inevitably avatāric and ecological

Visvāmitra: sage preceptor of Rāma and Lakṣmana; one-time rival of Vasiṣtha

Vivekānanda, Svāmī: (1863 – 1902): disciple of Śri Rāmakṛṣṇa Paramahaṁsa; founder of the Rāmakṛṣṇa order; reviver of Hindu and Indian spiritual self-confidence in our age

Vṛndāvana: sacred forest; site of Kṛṣṇa's mystic-erotic rite of dance with the milkmaids of Braja; powerful hope of the greening of existence

Yādavas: Kṛṣṇa's self-destructive clan; humanity?

INDEX

MORE ABOUT PENGUINS

For further information about books available from Penguins in India write to Penguin Books (India) Ltd, B4/246, Safdarjung Enclave, New Delhi 110 029.

In the UK: For a complete list of books available from Penguins in the United Kingdom write to Dept. EP, Penguin Books Ltd, Harmondsworth, Middlesex UB7 0DA.

In the U.S.A.: For a complete list of books available from Penguins in the United States write to Dept. DG, Penguin Books, 299 Murray Hill Parkway, East Rutherford, New Jersey 07073.

In Canada: For a complete list of books available from Penguins in Canada write to Penguin Books Canada Ltd, 2801 John Street, Markham, Ontario L3R 1B4.

In Australia: For a complete list of books available from Penguins in Australia write to the Marketing Department, Penguin Books Australia Ltd, P.O. Box 257, Ringwood, Victoria 3134.

In New Zealand: For a complete list of books available from Penguins in New Zealand write to the Marketing Department, Penguin Books (N.Z.) Ltd, Private Bag, Takapuna, Auckland 9.

UNVEILING INDIA:
A Woman's Journey
Anees Jung

The women in this book are neither extraordinary nor famous and yet their stories and testimonies provide a passionate, often deeply touching, revelation of what it means to be a woman in India today. They tell of marriage an widowhood, unfair work practices, sexual servitude, the problems of bearing and rearing children in poverty, religious discrimination and other forms of exploitation. But they also talk of fulfilling relationships, the joys of marriage and children, the exhilaration of breaking free from the bonds of tradition, ritual and religion. Taken as a whole, the book is essential reading for anyone wishing to understand the women of India—the silent majority that is now beginning to make itself heard.

'An extremely valuable investigation into the lives of ordinary women in India'
—*The Hindustan Times*

INDIAN JOURNALS

Allen Ginsberg

Allen Ginsberg writes: '*Indian Journals* are notebook writings sketches dream fragments night thoughts afternoon reveries Kodak snapshots optical & verbal: hymns to Kali, political ravings, one line pensées, doodles, descriptions in detail of opium dens in Calcutta & Bombay; fragments of conversations with beggars, poets, babas, newsmen, lovers; paragraphs of letters, ganja-grass high notations on moving trains and in burning grounds, tourist awes & addresses, glimpses of bridges and streets, but mostly the tortured introspection of self wandering in XX Century throughout northern India, living half a year at a time in Benares and Calcutta, dreaming about holymen and visiting some few, watching beggars, feeding lepers with Orlovsky poet-nurse, bathing in Ganges, shopping in ancient markets and cooking hideous cannibal chickens in holytown, learning mantras & Hindu gods' names for chanting; books of thought kept at fancy leisure, crude poems, home-made photos of cows and sadhus.'

'Unconventional, witty, grotesque, queer, obscure—undefinable.'

—*National Mail (Bhopal)*